Practical Shooting Scene Investigation

The Investigation and Reconstruction of Crime Scenes Involving Gunfire

by

Dean H. Garrison, Jr.

Practical Shooting Scene Investigation:
The Investigation and Reconstruction
of Crime Scenes Involving Gunfire

Universal Publishers/uPUBLISH.com
USA • 2003

ISBN: 1-58112- 576-3

www.uPUBLISH.com/books/garrison.htm

Preface

This book is for crime scene investigators who work shooting cases. It is not for detectives, whose job it is to interview witnesses and interrogate suspects. It is not for police officers, whose job it is to keep the peace, maintain order, arrest criminals, and secure crime scenes. It is not for attorneys (prosecution or defense) whose job it is to persuade a jury that their position is the right one, whether or not it actually is. It is a book for the crime scene investigator, whose job it is to record and collect evidence and generally figure out what happened at the scenes of shootings. Detectives, cops, and lawyers could learn a thing or two from this book, but it is not *for* them.

As in all criminal cases, the really important work takes place in the first few hours. Years later, attorneys argue about what the crime scene investigator did in those first moments, whether everything was done, if it was done right, and what might have been done differently. Judges have to hear motions and render opinions about routine crime scene photos. Jurors, many of whom have never been touched by crime, gape and squirm as they look at pictures that are nothing more than standard practice for the crime scene investigator. A crime scene processed carelessly or improperly has far-reaching effects, both in crippling a criminal case and in falsely implicating innocent persons.

As any crime scene investigator knows well, everyone is an expert. Every lawyer, every supervisor, and every private citizen who ever watched a cops'n'robbers movie or television show or ever read a paperback mystery knows exactly how crime scene work should be done . . . and they will tell anyone who will listen their personal opinion about their vast knowledge of the field. Crime lab people, many of whom do nothing more than open evidence envelopes, operate microscopes or chromatographs, and type reports, have very definite opinions about how crime scene people should behave. Professors of forensic science, some of whom have never been any closer to a bloodstain than their last nose bleed, will talk (and write) at length about how crime scene investigation should be run. As any crime scene investigator knows, the only people who seem to know nothing whatsoever about crime scene work are the police administrators who are supposed to provide the budget, personnel, and training for crime scene investigation.

This text was written in the United States by an American (*North* American), but I trust that other investigators will find it helpful. I know I have found a great deal of useful information on the subject of shooting investigation from authors in India, Germany, and Britain. I know that investigators in Scotland and Canada have utilized some of my research. I have found that the British spend a lot of time on gunshot residue analysis, the Israelis reenact and videotape shooting crimes, the Canadians spent a lot of time on poaching cases, and the Japanese experience fewer shootings annually in their nation than do most U.S. cities. While America has tried to shed its cowboy image and its gangster history, we remain the gunfight capital of the world. Investigators from other countries don't encounter in a lifetime the number of shooting cases that most American crime scene people work in a single summer. Most of what we all know about shooting investigation and reconstruction naturally (and unfortunately) comes from the United States. So it is with this book and its author. I hope the international readership will forgive the occasional "Americanism" in my words and the references to the peculiarities of the American legal and criminal justice systems.

This book is designed and intended as a very nuts and bolts practical guide to crime scene investigations involving shootings. It is not meant to cover the subjects of gunshot wounds, bloodstain analysis, general homicide investigation, crime laboratory procedure, or interview and interrogation techniques. It is a street guide. And I hope you find it useful.

I would like to acknowledge the support and encouragement of Jim Hamby of the Indianapolis-Marion County Crime Lab, Dave Brundage of the Illinois State Police lab system, Captain Tom Bevel (retired) of the Oklahoma City Police Department, Max Courtney of Fort Worth, Texas, Captain James Farris and Captain Pam Carrier of the Grand Rapids Police Department, and Brian Reed, Annie King (ret.), Rick Litts, and Cecile Herald of the GRPD Forensic Services Unit.

Dean H. Garrison, Jr.

TABLE OF CONTENTS

Introduction

The on-scene investigation of events and the reconstruction of those events almost always happen together. That is to say, reconstruction is a function of crime scene work. It is not laboratory work. At times, one needs to call out experts from the crime lab to come to the scene to figure out an event, but then they become crime scene people doing crime scene work. The term *reconstruction* has a mysterious ring to it, but all it really involves is the use of sound scientific thinking to figure out how an event occurred. Shooting reconstruction is a crime scene function, just like bloodstain analysis and traffic accident reconstruction. Only an idiot or an imposter would think of trying to reconstruct a shooting, an accident, or a crime without visiting the scene. Shooting investigation and reconstruction is often rightly associated with the firearm or "ballistics" sections of crime laboratories, although a person permanently buried in the depths of a crime lab, doing "bench work," seldom has much time for real, everyday crime scene work.

Within the discipline of criminalistics there are three somewhat indistinct and kindred categories involving firearms. The first involves the function, safety, and mechanical operation of guns, or what might be called "firearms engineering." The second is firearms identification, which is the determination that a particular firearm did or did not fire a particular bullet or cartridge case. The third is shooting reconstruction, that part of crime scene reconstruction involving the examination of the circumstances and physical evidence from the scene of a shooting to ascertain how the incident occurred.

Back in 1970, Steve Molnar, Jr. of the Ohio State Bureau of Criminal Investigation wrote in the *Association of Firearm and Tool Mark Examiners Journal*:

> "...we find ourselves being drawn into areas of firearms expertise that are removed from the microscopic comparisons of bullets and cartridge cases...like the function of the firearm, possibility of malfunctions, distance and angle of shots, where was the gun when it was fired, velocity of bullets, ricochets, etc. Even the police may question a version of a shooting."

Barry Fisher's *Techniques of Crime Scene Investigation* puts it this way:

> "...the investigation should decide whether the statements of the criminal are consistent. In the first statement, a criminal often makes consciously incorrect statements about personal actions in order to create extenuating circumstances. Those who investigate the scene of a crime have an opportunity to produce such an accurate reconstruction of the actual course of events that such an attempt by the criminal cannot succeed."

This then is essentially the realm of shooting investigation and reconstruction. It sometimes utilizes information about a weapon's mechanical functioning or lab reports about which ammunition was fired in which weapons, but shooting reconstruction generally relies on physical evidence in the form of trajectory, deflection, penetration, ricochet; the interaction of a projectile with walls, vehicles, windows, or flesh; and is often dependent on the position, location, and condition of items within the shooting *scene*. It has also been termed "projectile trajectory pattern" reconstruction [see *Lee, Henry* in the **Bibliography**].

Information about firearms design and function is available in countless history books, magazines, owner's manuals, and gunsmithing texts. Information about firearms identification can be found in a few renowned texts (*Hatcher, Burrard*, etc.) and, of course, years of *Journals* from the Association of Firearm and Toolmark Examiners. However, shooting reconstruction as a category appears here and there in various criminalistics texts, technical articles, and non-fiction books about specific criminal cases. With that in mind, this book addresses the particular realm of on-scene shooting investigation and reconstruction.

As it turns out, if one processes a shooting scene properly, the shooting reconstruction can be done at a later time by others. Let's say that Evidence Technician Jack is a good technician, who has an interest in fingerprint evidence or bloodstain evidence, but is not particularly interested in shooting investigation. If Jack were to work a shooting scene and process the evidence according to the methods outlined in this book, someone else, Jill from the crime lab, for instance, with more interest and more knowledge in shooting investigation could take Jack's crime scene photographs, measurements, and evidence and, after visiting the actual crime scene, could conduct a shooting reconstruction. This, of course, assumes that there was a sufficient amount of physical evidence in the beginning to reconstruct the event. Jill might have all the interest in the world, but if the killer shot the victim in a thunder storm, which washed the blood away, and he used a revolver that didn't ejected a case, and the bullet caused a through-and-through wound and was never found, because the victim ran to another location after the shooting, and the whole scene was overrun by a huge crowd of onlookers, none of whom saw anything. . .well there's not much that either Jack or Jill could do scene-wise. It would be up to Mutt, the medical examiner, to determine a bullet path through the victim's body, and Jeff, the detective, to locate the victim's estranged wife or the drug dealer he owed money or his current girlfriend's ex-husband (or some variation). . .and hope for a tearful confession or, at least, a damaging admission. But, scene-wise, there is not much to reconstruct.

Conversely, if Evidence Tech Jack is a lazy goof and screws up the scene work all by himself, there's not going to be much that anyone can reconstruct anyway. This book assumes that the reader is already well grounded in the proper processing of crime scenes. [It is suggested that the reader should already have read Fisher's *Techniques of Crime Scene Investigation*, Geberth's *Practical Homicide Investigation*, and Osterberg & Ward's *Criminal Investigation: A Method for Reconstructing the Past*.] It is also assumed that the reader possesses enough interest and enthusiasm to recognize that this book is neither the beginning nor the end of his or her education on the subject. The truly interested reader should explore the bibliography at the back of this book.

*   *   *

Chapter One

Some Basic Terms and Pitfalls of Shooting Scene Work

The Words We Use
In the movies, they're called "slugs," but in real life they are called *bullets* or *projectiles*. The terms "bullet hole" and "ricochet" don't mean much once you leave the theatre and enter the courtroom. Human beings are not "winged" by bullets; they are *wounded*. The word "gun" doesn't mean much in a world of *derringers, revolvers, pump-action shotguns, semiautomatic pistols, submachine guns, assault rifles, anti-tank weapons, and deck cannon.* Part of overcoming the pre-conceived notions and outright myths that jurors typically bring with them into the courtroom is the language of shooting investigation. One needs to teach the attorneys, the judge, and jury the right terms for things. This does not mean that one should befuddle the trial record with overly technical jargon, which leaves the court reporter searching dictionaries and jurors scratching their heads. But one must speak accurately and clearly. And much of this involves using the proper terms.

A bullet flying through a window has *perforated* that window, not "penetrated" it. A bullet entering a wall has *penetrated* that wall and may have *perforated* a mirror on the wall. The difference between penetration (going *into* something) and perforation (going *through* something) is important. (I have heard it explained this way: "In romance, if you're doing it right, no one gets *perforated*.") The aforementioned wall is called a *target* (an object struck by a projectile), which in no way means that anyone really meant to hit that target, only that it was hit. If the wall is the last object struck, it might be called a *terminus* (the place where the bullet ends up) or can be termed a "final target." The aforementioned mirror on this wall was struck by the bullet's passage, so it is technically a "target," but more precisely, it is an *intermediate target*. If the bullet path (which is not called a "trajectory") lines up between the perforation of the window, the secondary perforation of the mirror, and the penetration of the wall, these marks, holes, and traces can be called *corresponding defects*; that is, they all appear to be the result of a single bullet's path. If they cannot be aligned, they are just *defects*, and might be from separate shots. The hole on the outside of the window, where the bullet entered the glass, can be called an *in-shoot* or *entrance defect*, if one wants to discuss the differences between the small exterior in-shoot and the large interior *out-shoot* or *exit defect*. The elongated hole in the mirror that tells us the bullet had already started tumbling in flight from its encounter with the window is called a *keyhole* defect.

If the bullet is protruding from the wall, it is said to be *embedded* (or *imbedded*) in the wall. If the bullet penetrates the wall and knocks plaster off the opposite side without going through, it is said to have *spalled* the wall. If the bullet strikes the edge of a lamp on its way from the window to the wall, it may leave a *deflection defect*, such as a *skip* or *skid* (brief shallow marks), a *furrow* or *trench* (longer deeper marks), or *chunk-out* (where a piece of the lamp flies away). If that little piece of lamp, now called a *secondary projectile*, were to strike a nearby candle and leave a mark on it, the mark on the candle could be called a *secondary projectile defect*. This is only important if someone else has confused the defect on the candle with the direct bullet path; then one explains to them, "No, that is not a bullet defect, it is a secondary projectile defect." Many times these fine distinctions are only important (as was the case with the in-shoot and out-shoot on the window) when someone misunderstands or misinterprets the evidence. Someone may notice that the bulb on the aforementioned lamp is broken. The investigator examines the lamp and can see that the bulb was not broken by a direct strike of the bullet but by the bullet's strike to the lamp; he knows that the bulb was cracked indirectly by what is called a *sympathetic fracture*. The most common site for sympathetic fractures (and it often leads novices astray) is a window frame or storm door. There is a defect on the window frame and the nearby glass is broken through sympathetic fracture, but the inexperienced observer attributes the broken glass to a second projectile.

If the bullet is recovered from the wall all in one piece, it is *intact*. If the bullet's shape indicates some damage from its travels, it is *deformed*. If it is smashed all out of shape, one could call it *greatly deformed*. If a piece of the bullet is found on the floor, the piece is a *bullet fragment* or *jacket fragment* (in the case of stripped off bullet jackets). And jacket fragments should not gratuitously be termed "copper jackets." If one finds a very small piece of some shiny metal at the scene of a shooting, but cannot tell if it's a bullet part, the piece should be called a *metal* (or metallic) *fragment* (and let the crime lab figure it out). This is especially important in a scene where the fragment could be a tiny shaving from a lead bullet, a piece from an air-gun pellet, or a deformed piece of shotshell pellet.

Outside the shot-up house, one finds an ejected *cartridge case* or *casing*; the phrase "shell casing" is redundant but popular. The best description of the cartridge case, in addition to the headstamp markings of caliber and manufacturer, is to call it "fired," as opposed to "spent." Some people mistakenly refer to fired bullets as "spent bullets," when in fact a *spent* bullet is one that has lost all of its energy (i.e., fallen harmlessly to the ground). So it is better to go with "fired" and just leave the "spending" out of it.

In all of this language business, it is important to teach the attorneys (for both sides) what things are called and not called. It helps everyone involved if the lawyers stop referring to pistols as "revolvers" and pistol magazines as "clips" and cartridges as "bullets" and deflection sites as "ricochets" and sympathetic fractures from secondary projectiles as "four more bullet holes." If the attorneys can't comprehend the terminology well enough to formulate a question, how can we expect jurors to follow the testimony?

Pitfalls and Pratfalls for the Unwary

Several recurring problems (myths, gremlins, what have you) hound the crime scene investigator at a shooting scene. Some of these problems, gunshot sounds for example, come from the incident's witnesses and participants. Other problems, such as bullet hole size information, come from the preconceived notions of police officers. Sometimes our own preconceived notions can get in the way of an effective investigation, just like the preconceived notions of jurors (from television, movies, or something Uncle Ralph once told them) can hinder their understanding of the evidence.

Gunfire Sound Information

One evening, after dark, the police are dispatched to a complaint of a shotgun being fired. A second caller reports shots being fired from a moving car. A third caller reports something "that sounds like a car backfiring." A police officer in a patrol car hears some of the shots north of the location. Another officer reports that the shots "sound more like .22s" and are coming from west of the initial complaint call. A police sergeant reports that he is behind the car doing the shooting. Other officers race to the scene. A felony stop is made on the suspect vehicle. With the driver out of the vehicle and handcuffed, the officers search the car. No weapons are found. Once things are calmed down, the suspect shows the officers how his engine backfires when the engine is revved. The officers relax a little; it's only a backfiring car. During the demonstration, a neighbor calls to report police officers in the street having a gun battle.

In the above example, only the third caller, who reported sounds "like a car backfiring," was correct. Everyone else jumped to conclusions. For the officers, these sorts of reports should be taken seriously for their own safety. However, depending on the neighborhood and its history of gunfire, some people will report gunfire "that sounds like a car backfiring," some people will report a car backfiring "that sounds like gun shots," and some will report "machinegun fire down the street." It's really a crapshoot, the variety of reports one gets in regard to gunshot sound. It's important to notice that police officers are only slightly better than your average Joe when it comes to identifying and interpreting such sound.

If one gets 27 neighbors all reporting one gunshot, it is probably a single shot. If two or more shots are fired, the likelihood of 27 or even seven neighbors reporting the number correctly is next to impossible. Some hear one and others hear twelve. Sometimes a neighbor sleeps through the first three shots, wakes up during the next two shots, hears only the sixth shot, and calls the police, reporting that he "heard a shot." People, especially children, sleep through gunfire all the time. Some people, while reporting they "didn't hear nothin," simply mean they are not going to tell *you* what they heard. Other people, desperately seeking attention and involvement in the police investigation, will conjure up all sorts of useless sound misinformation. Young officers will sometimes do this, thinking about what they heard, processing that information along with the reports of others, and telling you what the results of what they think they heard, rather than what actually entered their ears. Consider the fact that experience police officers involved in gunfights, either as bystanders or shooters or intended targets, very, very often have wrong information when it comes to the actual number of shots fired. They're right at the scene; they have experience with guns and gunfire; they may even be in sight of the muzzle flashes. Yet they still get in wrong.

Some witnesses (and this includes some cops) will report the quality of a gunshot sound. A frequent scenario is an ear-witness who says something like, "I was in the Army, and I know what I heard was an automatic." People will say they *heard* a shotgun, and they *know* it was a shotgun sound, because they *own* a shotgun. Persons who are familiar with guns and gunshot sounds are sometimes helpful ear-witnesses, but are often as confused as anyone else; they just won't admit readily admit it. Some people will say they "heard a .38" or they "heard a nine (millimeter)," when they don't really mean actually weapon calibers; it's just their way of vaguely referring to handgun shots in general. People in violence-plagued neighborhoods will hear shots and say they "heard an AK-47" (assault rifle), while people in rural areas might report the same shots by saying that they "heard a .30-30." People bring their own histories and biases to bear on their ears in a shooting.

One thing that ear-witnesses seem to get right is the distinction between two very different weapons in a gunfight. They will report, "I heard pop, pop, pop, and then a boom." This could be the result of a shooter moving closer to their listening post or swinging the weapon in their direction or may involve two shots fired inside a vehicle with a third shot outside; but when one gets "pop and boom" reports from different ear-witnesses in different locations, one should take note. The same can be said of reports wherein witnesses note a pause between several shots. They say, "I heard two and then nothing and then three more" or "I heard a bang and then a pause and then a two pops." When multiple ear-witnesses are reporting a pause, it's worth remembering.

Reports of the direction from which gunfire came can confuse an investigation. A neighbor can say that "It was right outside my house; I heard the window rattle," while a homeowner down the block reports the same thing. Anyone who has stood on a street corner in a busy downtown intersection, listening to an approaching ambulance siren and trying to guess where it's coming from and where it's going, has seen that sounds and their echoes can be confusing. Imagine trying to make an estimate of direction with gunfire, where there is no sustained sound information (as with the siren example), but simply one quick shot. Because closer shots sound louder, people will report that louder shots occurred closer. How many times have police officers responded to sound of shots fired "down by the corner" only to look around and find nothing? They leave, write their reports, and get called back to a "man down with gunshot wound" a block and a half away. The direction of gunfire sound and its proximity are, at best, approximations. One should try to find the old lady witness who just happened to look out her window and see the muzzle flashes.

Bullet Defect Size

The size of a mark that a projectile leaves on an object is related to the material the object is made of, the shape and size of the projectile and the material it is made of, and the velocity of the projectile (which itself is a function of a cartridge's loading, the length of the weapon's barrel, the distance between the weapon and the object struck), and a slew of other weird things like paint surfaces, wood density, soft body tissue, intermediate targets, glass tempering, ammunition manufacture variations, and so on. Everybody, of course, is an expert when it comes to saying that such and such a hole was probably made by such and such a caliber bullet. With no other reliable crime scene information, bullet defect size simply doesn't matter much. Little tiny round holes are hardly ever made by shotgun slugs. Giant round holes are hardly ever made by BBs. And neither tiny nor giant round holes are made by throwing a boot. Alone, the information is, at best, material for estimation. This does not mean that scale photos and measurements should be neglected; such photos, accompanied by the location of casings, other projectiles, and a shooting victim, all make useful evidence. But one must be wary of the person who states a caliber of projectile that made a given bullet defect (based on size alone).

Ejection Patterns

Automatic and semiautomatic and pump-action weapons eject fired cartridge cases in different ways (left, right, front, rear, near, or far), depending on the weapon, the ammunition, the surface that the casing falls upon, the number or cops who have walked on the casings with their shoes, and apparently where the firearm decides to kick out a casing at that particular moment. Many weapons will eject thirty casings to the right but spill out the thirty-first one to the front. Some casings land nearby, while some roll away. Things get moved at crime scenes. Again, like bullet hole size information, ejection patterns are only for rough estimates. One should beware of a person who will state a shooter's position based on one or two ejected cartridge cases. Shootings inside cramped quarters, like crowded rooms, stairwells, and vehicle interiors, make ejection pattern data unreliable.

*   *   *

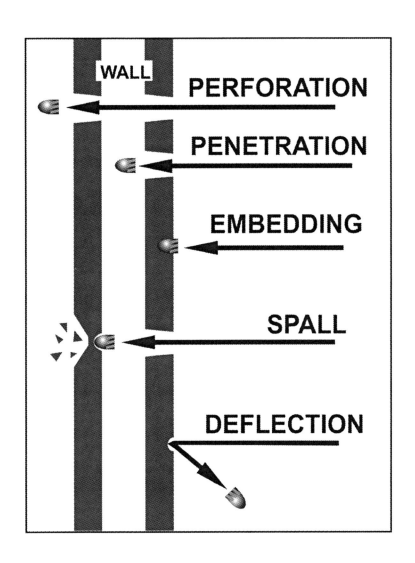

Chapter Two

Photographing the Shooting Scene

The proper recording of the condition, position, and location of bullet defects at crime scenes is essential to shooting reconstruction and subsequent courtroom proceedings. There is perhaps nothing quite as frustrating (and yet so common) as crime scene photographs that do not adequately document bullet defects. Either by lack of detail, lack of scale, or lack of reference, many shooting scene photographs are rendered useless to investigators and triers of fact.

Detail Photographs of the Bullet Hole's Condition

As we know from our study of research by Rathman[1] and Jordan et al[2], the bullet hole, whether it be a penetration or deflection defect, can tell us a lot about how it was made. More importantly, the bullet defect can often show us how it was *not* made, and criminal cases sometimes turn on such information.

A bullet hole demands as much photographic attention as a single hair or partial shoeprint at a crime scene. The same principles of multiple photos, angled lighting, and exposure bracketing apply. Bullet defects on items that you are *not* collecting as evidence should be photographed with the same care as a footwear impression. As with other three-dimensional impressions, a bullet defect has depth and, especially with ricochet sites, can reveal much about direction and incident angle. If the crime scene investigators follow the impression photography directions in footwear examination texts[3] or tire impression evidence texts[4], they should emerge from the scene with bullet hole photos that actually show meaningful detail. Color film recording of impression evidence is often not considered important; bullet hole photography, however, should have a color rendering, so that lead wipe, transfer evidence, and distinctions between paint layers on objects are not lost. An appropriate scale is, of course, critical to the photography of any bullet defect.

1.) Take close-up photos with film plane parallel to the struck surface.

2.) Take multiple exposures with oblique lighting at several angles.

3.) Use color film and a scale.

Photographs of the Bullet Hole's Position

Position is different from location. A dead man lying on the living room floor and the woman standing over him are in the same location but in different positions. The bullet holes in a closed door fired from the outside and the holes in the door made by bullets fired from the inside are in the same location but in different positions. While the close-up photograph of a bullet hole in a wall gives us detail, it appears on the final print as a blob free-floating in space. Hand someone a bullet hole close-up photo and watch them turn it round and round, trying to orient the picture to the scene, or hand it to them upside-down and notice how they can't tell the difference. These are the sorts of problems generated when a bullet hole's position is not properly photographed.

After those first general scene views are recorded and whatever necessary trace evidence collection is completed[5], the bullet defect should be marked and labeled, and then photographed again. You already have a scale in the photo; now you need to add a North arrow (on horizontal surfaces) or an Up arrow (on vertical surfaces). In scenes where projectiles strike two perpendicular surfaces, such as both the south and east walls of a room, it also helps to include in your labels the north-south or east-west directions. Some people spray paint huge numbers or great circles around their bullet holes and then stand back far enough to get the whole mess in their pictures. This technique seems to work best on bullet defects in trees, but can irritate homeowners who don't like graffiti. Some people take brightly colored evidence tape (yellow works well) and make a little box around the defect. They then write their initials, case number, bullet defect number, and Up arrow right on the tape. This works well on many surfaces and under most weather conditions (tape doesn't work well on trees in the winter). Better still is to make a triangle, instead of a square, with the tape, which turns the tape label into its own Up arrow.

For deflection defects (ricochet marks, skids, skips, "dings," or whatever you want to call them), it helps to affix a six- to 12-inch length of marking tape next to the defect but running in the same direction. This can not only help orient the person viewing the resulting photographs, but can help you at the scene when you're trying to find the bullet or terminal defect. Make sure you duplicate the long axis of the mark as carefully as you can.

The problem with numbering your bullet defects is that this is often interpreted as a sequencing of shots in a multiple-shot incident (i.e., Hole #7 was fired after Hole #4). Numbering also creates problems when a bullet strikes two items that you can definitely associate; you end up in court saying things like, "People's Exhibit Number 26 is my photograph of Defect #12 in the cabinet, which was made by the bullet coming through Hole #4 in the kitchen door, which appears in my photograph, People's Exhibit 18, which was the eighth shot to enter the residence." It is much better to letter your bullet holes, so that "A" is the hole in the window and "A-1" is the associated perforation of the kitchen door and "A-2" is the terminal defect in the kitchen cabinet. If you work a shooting scene where so many shots were fired that you run out of alphabet, then you've got other problems to worry about besides numbering versus lettering.

    1.) Place labeled orientation arrows (i.e., Up, North, Front, or directions) clearly in your bullet hole photos.

    2.) Label the defect with name, case number, date, defect letter or number, and any other information that might help you later when you are describing the scene to a jury.

Photographs of the Bullet Hole's Location

    A crime scene photograph of a police officer pointing to a bullet hole in a wall does not tell us much about the hole or the officer (except that he's patient). Somewhere between the macroscopic views of the holes and the area views of the neighborhood, there should be photographs that tell us where in the world the bullet hole is. The crime scene sketch is useful and necessary, but cannot make the visual connection that you've already started by showing the jury photographs. The area view photos (also called *environment shots*) are usually no problem for crime scene photographers. Many photographers just can't seem to cross the visual bridge between the house views and the bullet hole close-ups.

    As we've discussed, the terms *location* and *position* are different. At the intersection of Fifth and Elm, there is a two-car accident with one car on its roof: same location, different positions. The positions are important, of course, but if we only had close-ups of the cars and an aerial photo of the whole city, you would never learn about the streets Fifth and Elm, which are vital pieces of the puzzle. Somewhere the link must be completed.

If the tape triangles you made for the bullet hole labels are big enough, you are all set to take wide area views. If they're not, you can either move in closer or add a second width of tape to your triangles. If you don't have brightly colored evidence tape, you can cut one-foot lengths of crime scene barrier tape and make triangles around the bullet holes, holding them in place with fingerprint tape. (Or you can spray-paint great circles and numbers on the wall.) Photos taken perpendicular to the struck surface can show the bullet defects relative to a door or corner. Area views showing the bullet holes in the background and ejected cartridge cases in the foreground help the triers of fact follow your reasoning. Views of defects from witness positions or reconstructed shooter's positions are immensely helpful. In any case, the jurors should be able to look at a photo of the front of the house and see where the bullet hole markings are. The holes in the lampshade, the bookshelf, and the back door should all be marked and photographed so that the room's interior view shows not only the holes' relationships to each other, but also their relationship to the whole room.

Properly marked defects in properly composed photographs, along with a competent crime scene sketch, can help a jury understand how multiple defects are related, how a defect is related to a stain, how a defect is related to a body, or how it is all related to a bystander. Jurors can see why you think two defects were made by the same shot or how other defects are unrelated. And you spend less time explaining how the whole thing fits together, because your pictures of the condition, position, and location of the bullet defects will tell the story for you.

*   *   *

NOTES

1. Rathman, G.A., "The Effects of Material Hardness on the Appearance of Bullet Impact Damage," **AFTE Journal**, Vol. 20, No. 3, July 1988, pp. 300-305.

2. Jordan, G.E., Bratton, D.D., Donahue, H.C.H., and Rowe, W.F., "Bullet Ricochet from Gypsum Wallboard," **Journal of Forensic Sciences**, Vol. 33, No. 6, Nov. 1988, pp. 1477-1482.

3. Bodziak, W.J., **Footwear Impression Evidence**, Elsevier: NY, 1990.

4. McDonald, P., **Tire Imprint Evidence**, Elsevier: NY, 1989.

5. Patty, J., McJunkins, S. and Murdock, J., "Associating Recovered Bullets with Ricochet Sites," **AFTE Journal**, Vol. 7, No. 2, July 1975, pp. 28-32.

An organized photographic presentation helps jurors follow more of your subsequent testimony.

Chapter Three

Measuring the Shooting Scene

The measurement of crime scenes is an inexact art, suffering from several simultaneous handicaps. Certain measurements require an attention to detail in fractions of an inch (bullet defect locations or bloodstain drop-size). Certain other crime scene measurements (skidmarks or street widths) can be found to the nearest foot without any substantive damage to the truth. But the equipment used to make the measurements, the conditions under which the work is accomplished, and finally the people performing the work all conspire to make crime scene measurement an approximate science. This does not make it wrong; it can still produce diagrams that are both fair and accurate. But no one should kid themselves by ignoring the limitations of the crime scene sketch.

Investigators who use steel measuring tapes sometimes disparage their colleagues who use 100-foot cloth tapes, but the first time a steel tape is stepped on or run over by a car is the last time it is ever accurate and probably the last time it can be reeled back into its spool. Cloth tapes, on the other hand, get old and stretch; they rot away; they are a different length, depending on whether they're wet or dry. The investigators using cloth measuring tapes sometimes sneer at others who use measuring wheels, noting that lumpy pavement sometimes adds and sometimes takes away from the measured lengths; they point out that wheels do not work in grass or snow or ice. And folks who use wheels that measure in inches have opinions about people who use wheels that measure in tenths-of-a-foot. There are still some old traffic investigation measuring wheels, usually great spoked orange things that click off measurements to the nearest foot. Everyone makes fun of these things, but they did the job; and for many long accident scenes, they work quite well.

Investigators who triangulate all their measurements have little good to say about people who use the coordinate method. The triangulators like to point out that visually picking the 90-degree intersect of an item to a baseline is fool's work. The coordinate-method followers make two valid points about triangulation: 1.) it almost always requires two people, and 2.) it's easy to screw up when transferring measurements to a final drawing. The triangulators counter this by saying that, at some scenes, there are no curb-lines or building edges or civilized borders from which to coordinate; therefore, sometimes there is no choice but to triangulate. There are proponents of split-field rangefinders and sonic measurement systems and laser rangefinders and surveyor's transits. If a police officer measures an exterior house wall with a rolling tape and gets "40 feet" and a defense attorney's private investigator measures the same wall with a computerized laser surveying system and gets "38 feet 11 5/8 inches," who, besides a desperate defense attorney, is going to argue about it? It is still fair and fairly accurate, given the nature of the work.

Crime scene investigators make measurements under a variety of work conditions. There are frequent interruptions. There is often no one to help. If it is raining, the measurements still have to be made. If there are shots being fired in the neighborhood, the job still has to get done. The ground is uneven; the floors are covered with blood pools or trash or children's toys or evidence. The rooms sometimes suffer from so-called "ghetto architecture," with houses hastily chopped up into apartments that feature strangely angled walls, doors that go nowhere, stairways that just end, chocolate-colored wallpaper, and 25-watt bulbs in the hallways. Crime scene measurements are often made in an environment of trash, maggots, putrefying corpses, suffocating heat, bitter cold, and flies that feed on the body and then light on the investigator. There are those who would argue that this is where the crime scene investigator has chosen to work, so he or she should also make accurate measurements; this, of course, is true. The job should be done to the best of one's abilities. However, it is useful to recognize that some scenes lend themselves more easily to measurement than others. Measuring the clean mansions and gateways of heaven must certainly be easier than measuring the crime scene rooms in hell. (Heaven, I'm sure, is more forgiving of the crime scene measurer who loses a few inches here and there in the final sketch.) This is not to excuse poor work; this is only to help understand the limitations of crime scene measurement.

So, acknowledging that there are limitations to the accuracy of crime scene measurements, one must recognize some of the pitfalls specifically encountered when measuring the scene of a shooting scene. The following three figures demonstrate some of the problems of bullet path measurement and, I hope, are self-explanatory.

Finally, we have the limitations of the people doing the actual measurement work. If these people lack the basic skills, knowledge, and motivation to make good measurements, no amount of precision equipment and no clean, uncluttered, indoor, air-conditioned crime scene rooms will ever be enough to get decent measurements from such people. The motivation problem is a management issue and is beyond the scope of this text. The skills part is a matter of practice, how to get the right (necessary) eight or 28 or 138 measurements to accurately record the position and location of the crime scene and the evidence (and *more* is certainly not always better). There are those who say more measurements are always better, more dimensions, more photographs, and more details. More is worthless unless the *right* dimensions, the *necessary* photographs, and the *correct* details are not recorded. The skills necessary to recognize what are important measurements and what is a waste of time and effort, what needs to be photographed and what is photographic overkill, and what is evidence and what is merely area trash—these skills are learned from experience. The basic knowledge of how to measure crime scenes is learned from veteran investigators and thus can suffer from those people's lack of motivation, skills, and knowledge. One hears, "We've never done it that way before," or "We've always worked crime scenes like this." I believe it was bloodstain analyst Herbert MacDonell who put forth that, "No matter how many times you've done something wrong doesn't make it the right way to do things." A conscientious crime scene investigator must continue his or her education by reading and research, trying new things or new approaches to old problems, and by comparing notes with other investigators, preferably outside their own department. And one must be resourceful and sometimes creative. As Hans Gross said in his famous book, *Criminal Investigation*, "He who seeks to learn only when some notable crime turns up, will have great difficulty in learning anything at all." (You're reading; that's a start.)

* * *

SLIGHT VARIATIONS IN A VICTIM'S ESTIMATED HEAD POSITION CAN GREATLY AFFECT SHOT ANGLE

Care must be taken when estimating a shot angle from two defects that are so close together.

Chapter Four

Using Bullet Hole Probes

The proper use of bullet hole probes is essential to the effective investigation and reconstruction of shooting incidents. Carelessness or the employment of inappropriate probes can produce inaccurate data and taint an investigation. Bullet hole examination is a *crime scene* operation and, like any early stage of an investigation, can affect all that comes later in the process. Likewise, errors made in the beginning are magnified because of their propensity to misdirect an inquiry at its onset. This is not to imply that the crime scene investigator should or even could have all the correct information about a crime at the start of the scene work, only that the crime scene work itself should not add to the swirl of misinformation.

The idea of using probes to indicate a bullet's path is sound, but the method of the probe user must also be sound. The most interesting aspect of bullet hole probe technique— even some *bad* techniques—is that it tells us almost immediately where the bullet did ***not*** come from, which can be a valuable bit of knowledge to have early in an investigation. We don't know when or where a detective first stuck a pencil into a bullet hole to get an idea of where an offending bullet originated. Pencils and pens, unless they are exceptionally long, of a true bullet hole diameter, and accurately centered, do not make adequate probes. The pencils of detectives are for note-taking, not hole probing. Detectives still do it, of course; but then detectives can occasionally be caught with their pencils inside gun barrels, too.

Bullet hole probes have been constructed of various materials over the years. Medical examiners often use stainless steel or aluminum rods to indicate wound tracks; these probes are washable, but sometimes too heavy to be left freestanding in bullet holes. Tubing made of copper or aluminum is bendable and, once bent, is unusable ever after. Glass rods are lightweight and handy, but tend to break and are difficult to photograph. Drinking straws can be very useful under the right circumstances, but are generally not long enough or sturdy enough for most crime scene work. Arrow shafts can be used. Wood dowels are well suited for probe work, in that they are available in a wide variety of diameters, can easily be trimmed to fit, and can be painted a color that will contrast with their surroundings. Wooden rods, however, can warp with moisture and wear. For a few dollars, a selection of dowels can be purchased, sealed against moisture, painted Safety Yellow or Hunter Orange, and replaced as necessary. Stiff plastic probes are commercially available in a limited assortment of diameters and usually only in black or white. As shooting scenes frequently require the simultaneous use of several same-size probes, the use of commercial models can be expensive. A combination of straight wood dowels, plastic probes, and a couple drinking straws is a good beginning for the crime scene technician's bullet probe kit.

Having a wide variety of probe diameters sounds important but isn't. Bullet holes come in a hodgepodge of sizes, more sizes than there are bullet calibers, which are more diameters than you can ever match with sticks and rods. Bullet holes can be keyholes, can start small and end big, or can grow (as in windows) before you ever get a chance to probe them. It is much more important that a probe be properly centered in a bullet hole or defect than it is to find a probe to exactly match the diameter of the hole. Because bullet, pellet, and fragment holes can be quite small, a few very thin probes should be available; these slender probes must be checked frequently, as they are especially prone to warpage.

There are three basic methods for centering a probe in a bullet hole: floating the probe, enlarging the diameter of the probe to fit the hole, and reducing the diameter of the hole to fit the probe. The first involves suspending the probe in mid air at the hole's center, either hanging it from strings, clamping it to a camera tripod, or in some other way supporting its weight. This is usually difficult, but seldom necessary. It comes in handy when the bullet perforation site appears in something fragile (i.e., clothing, plant leaves, curtains) that will not support the probe's weight alone. The second method, probe enlargement can be achieved by applying a band of tape around the probe and gradually increasing its diameter until it fits the hole. A probe run through a rubber stopper or through the axis of a small Styrofoam cone can also be useful.

The final method of probe centering is hole size reduction, which is the most adaptable. This technique involves affixing a sheet of heavy paper (cardboard, manila envelope, plastic sheet protector, etc.) over the bullet hole, making a small perforation in the sheet over the center of the larger entry, and running an undersized probe through this artificial aperture. Sometimes it is helpful to make the hole in the cover sheet first, so you can see what you're doing. Clear plastic sheets work well, if they are sturdy enough to support the probe's weight alone; these also make photographing the whole thing a lot easier.

It seems painfully obvious to say that probe usage requires *two* fixed points that a bullet has marked in its passage. The exterior in-shoot defect is usually obvious but, with many wall shots, the second fixed point is inside the wall and difficult to explore. In some cases, a light shone through the outer hole will reveal the location of the inner mark (or even additional marks). When this is not possible, a section of the wall adjacent to the bullet hole, preferably below or to one side, should be excavated. Because inner wall defects are as important to probe orientation as exterior in-shoot defects, the interior marks should be recorded with measurements and, if at all possible, photography. While probe fit is desirable, probes should not be force-fitted into bullet holes. Alteration of the in-shoot should be avoided; likewise, the secondary internal defect should not be harmed. At times, especially with shots fired through ceiling panels or shots fired from inside a dwelling through an exterior window, the second necessary fixed point is not available. An examination of the out-shoot defect is sometimes helpful, but probes seldom work under these circumstances. There must be a second fixed point--not just a guess as to where it is--in order for probes to be used; bullet path reconstructions utilizing one fixed point and one unfixed zone are for establishing areas of gunfire and require strings and/or laser, not bullet hole probes.

Straws are useful as probes in materials such as insulation, foam padding, and upholstery, where the bullet track has partially collapsed on itself. Penlights with bore lamp attachments can be directed through straws to help with the insertion and placement of probes. Air forced through a hollow probe will clear plaster dust and other debris from bullet defect sites inside a wall. With patience and careful alignment, a laser can be aimed down the center of an installed probe, lengthening the perceived axis of the probe without the usual complication of strings.

All of this assumes that the basic preliminary crime scene work has been completed. The scene is photographed environmentally, in detailed close-ups, and in several views that establish the relationship between critical items within the scene. Three photos—one showing only a firearm, one showing only an ejected cartridge case, and one showing only a bullet hole—are not very useful in shooting reconstruction, nor do they make a very meaningful presentation for court. The spatial relationship between items of evidence is often more important than the mere photographic recording of any one item alone. The *in situ* photographs are the most constructive for reconstruction. Decisions should be made about trace evidence collection, bloodstain patterns, residue collection, and control samples. The scene should be measured for a crime scene sketch and should include elevation measurements of hole centers, probe angles, and movable items, taking into account discrepancies in ground levels, floor levels, and stairways. Additional photographs, including items on the ground with numbered or lettered photo markers, defects on upright items highlighted with tape or marker (to include Up direction, defect number, and incident/investigator designation), and scale or 1:1 pictures of defects, should be completed before walls are excavated and things are altered. It is often useful to take instant photos for the medical examiner's office. Finally, witness views, assuming that some witness information has been developed, can be photographed. The basics need to be taken care of first.

Besides the aforementioned tapes and markers, the shooting investigator should have a supply of strings, cords, thread, high-strength fishing line, nails, screws, tacks, eye screws, washers, and clothes pins. Equipment should include at least two camera tripods and a couple of sturdy lighting stands (not for lights, but for supporting bullet path strings). Compass, framing square, inclinometer, protractors (clear plastic and disposable cardstock), level, plumb line, and clear plastic centering templates should be available.

With the right equipment, sufficient time, and attention to detail, the investigator can use bullet hole probes effectively at the crime scene and contribute both to the reconstruction of the shooting and the resolution of the case.

*   *   *

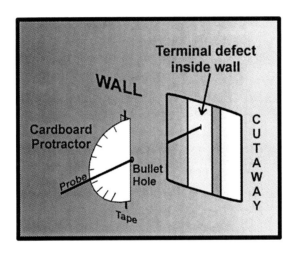

Terminal defect inside wall

WALL

Cardboard Protractor

Probe

Bullet Hole

Tape

C U T A W A Y

A probe properly installed will connect both the external and hidden internal defects.

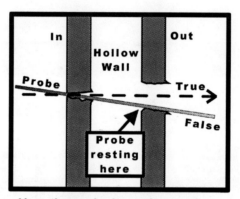

Here the probe is resting on the
bottom of a perforation, which
tilts the shot angle and ruins
the analysis.

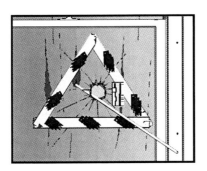

This probe requires
support on the large hole
in the glass and the
perforated curtain inside.

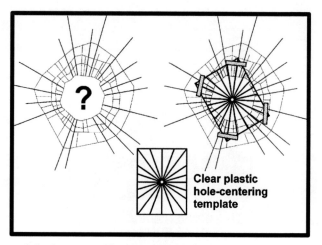

Clear plastic
hole-centering
template

A hole-centering template can be used
and photographed with its lines on top of
the radial fractures of a window.

Drinking straws can be used when one needs to run a string or laser through an upholstered object.

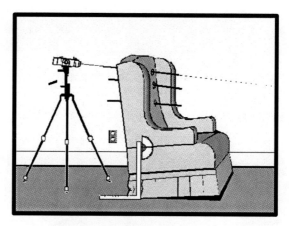

Here the angle that the chair was tipped at the moment of the shooting can be determined by laser alignment through straws in the padding.

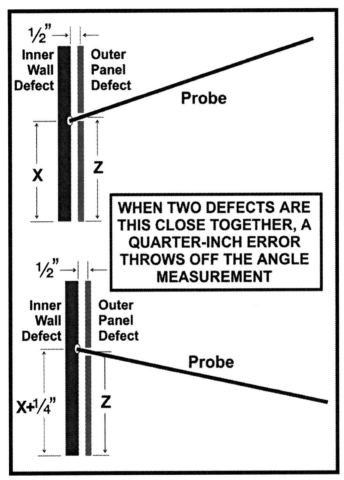

½"

Inner
Wall
Defect

Outer
Panel
Defect

Probe

X

Z

WHEN TWO DEFECTS ARE
THIS CLOSE TOGETHER, A
QUARTER-INCH ERROR
THROWS OFF THE ANGLE
MEASUREMENT

½"

Inner
Wall
Defect

Outer
Panel
Defect

Probe

$X+¼"$

Z

Two defects that are very close together are
unreliable in providing a shot angle estimate.

Chapter Five

Scenes With Unfixed Targets

In estimating where a bullet came from or where it flew, we try to find two or more fixed objects that the projectile perforated, penetrated, or marked. At times we have a hole in a window and a second hole in a wall; we align these and try to estimate the shooter's location. Other times we have only a hole in a window and a witness statement of the shooter's approximate location; then we line up these two points and try to find the bullet. Quite often, however, the bullet marked or perforated only one fixed object and passed through one unfixed object (i.e., curtain, coat sleeve, or open doorway), and we have no input—or **false** input—from witnesses concerning possible shooter locations. Intermediate objects are frequently moved or damaged beyond repair. In these common cases, we can use the fixed object as an anchor and narrow down the vertical and horizontal parameters of the one unfixed intermediate target, providing a zone or range of possible gunfire sources.

Of course, sometimes an elongated in-shoot or a penetration of sufficient depth into a single fixed object can indicate the directionality of a bullet path[1]. This short, albeit valuable, shot angle guide should not be overlooked; bullet hole probes of appropriate diameter are necessary. To overlook such a plainly apparent clue would be foolhardy. An equally appalling pitfall is to associate two bullet defects with a single shot when this is not supported by the evidence; assigning undue significance to marks made by different shots indicates unclear thinking. There must be discernible and definable reasons that one thinks two defects were the result of a single bullet's passage.

We are using the term *bullet path* here to avoid confusing the relatively short range of most crime scene shootings with the word *trajectory*, which is variously described as "the curved path of a projectile from muzzle to target"[2], "the curve of the path the bullet describes during its course of flight"[3], and the "flight characteristics of projectiles fired under prescribed conditions at various elevations"[4]. Crime scene bullet paths and so-called "straight-line trajectories" are usually of such short distance that bullet drop and line-of-bore considerations are virtually negligible and seldom relevant to the event in question. Also, we will not address the subject of human bodies, those most unfixed and unpredictable of intermediate targets, whose proclivities at bullet deflection, velocity loss, and energy absorption are ascertained with varying degrees of certainty by medical examiners. We will not pretend to know all the ins and outs of tissue, bones, and organs with regard to bullet passage. Let the medical examiners, emergency room doctors, and the assorted wound ballistics experts debate these points[5].

Unfixed intermediate targets take many forms: curtains, closing screen doors, or moving car windows; and sometimes blankets, shirt sleeves, or the leaves of a plant. At times an ajar door, open window, or blown-out windshield provides the intermediate "target" at a crime scene. Things fall and break, doors are thrown open, shades are closed, and scenes are altered, but sometimes a range of estimated shooter's locations can be determined. . .with care.

One must try, first of all, to determine what has been moved or altered at the crime scene. Experience has taught us that, despite our best efforts to freeze them in time, many crime scenes are altered and/or destroyed by the time we can search, examine, and record them. It seems to be the nature of the beast that humans—be they victims, witnesses, ambulance attendants, or cops—tend to muddy up crime scenes with their activities. When this involves life-saving measures or the disarming of suspects, the activity is far more important than any crime scene reconstruction efforts. When a scene is tampered with or otherwise altered, through negligence or carelessness, this is unforgivable but all too common[6]. It seems to be human nature; it must be accounted for but not excused. It must be remembered, however, that a shooting reconstructionist, whether for the prosecution **or** defense, must deal with the same crime scene contamination and must temper their estimations and conclusions accordingly. The crime scene, as found, must obviously be photographed and measured for a sketch. The bullet holes, keyholes, and other defects (marks, skids, ricochets, etc.) must be examined and recorded properly. The scene must be searched and evaluated *beyond* what the witnesses claim and what the detectives say. As in all reconstruction, the statements of witnesses must be tested by the physical evidence at the crime scene, *not* the other way around[7].

In attempting to replace an unfixed intermediate target in its original position—be it a window shade, curtain, or vehicle—one can ask a witness who has some idea of the object's position prior to the crime. This is helpful, but by no means the end of the inquiry. Moved items of furniture may have left impressions in carpets; an outline in dust may indicate where an object once rested; tire tracks can help establish the position and location of a shot vehicle that has since been moved. These indicators must be explored. One must also establish the physical boundaries in which the item

<u>could</u> have been located. For example, a shot window shade might extend from only six inches below the top of a given window frame to three inches above the sill, and <u>not</u> include the whole 24 inches of the exposed window. A vehicle's position is limited by curb lines; a floor lamp's position is limited by surrounding furniture.

Ranges should be ascertained when possible. By "ranges" here, we do not mean muzzle-to-target distance, but *areas of possible sources of gunfire*, sometimes called "shooter's position" or "origin of trajectory." This might be a variable—horizontal, vertical, or often both (3-D)—zone or *area of uncertainty* from which a shot likely came into the scene. One must have, of course, at least one fixed terminus or intermediate target and one unfixed but limitable terminus or intermediate target to establish the parameters. With two hugely unknown parameters (i.e., a running man shot through an open garage door), one ends up with an area of uncertainty that include shots fired from passing bicycles *and* low-flying airplanes.

To visualize and measure a zone, say from a hole in an interior wall back through a blown out window, a laser or laser pointer works well[8]. With the laser placed at the terminus, one fires the beam back through the four corners of the window, while an assistant marks the corners of the source area in the next room, the yard, or street. These, then, are measured and photographed. Not everyone has a laser. Stretched crime scene barrier tape or clothesline can be anchored at the terminal defect and stretched tightly back through the unfixed intermediate area to establish a zone; this is good for photography, but requires a strong anchor point and some helpers. For those who are equipped with neither lasers nor helpers, a 100-yard package of dental floss in the crime scene kit is very useful; the floss is lightweight, durable, and easy to tighten, but does not photograph well. The zone's corners, however, can be outlined by numbered or lettered photo markers or cones, and this area can be photographed to show its relationship to the scene. Proper measurement of both top and elevation views can outline the source area of a particular shot.

Establishing a two- or three-dimensional zone from which gunfire originated, especially if that zone is large, is not often immediately recognized as useful by attorneys (prosecution *or* defense). These advocates are slow to comprehend that knowing where the zone is located automatically gives them some very solid knowledge of where the shooter *could not have been* at the time of the gunfire. This is sound evidence that can be used to verify witnesses' claims and counter an opposing attorney's allegations. Furthermore, if one examines many source-of-gunfire zones at crime scenes, one is struck by the fact that the zone often dramatically limits the possible positions of adult shooters, whether firing from shoulder, hip, prone position, or from car windows. Once a source zone is determined, many wild suggestions cease to sound credible.

The uncertain elements of one's estimation must be acknowledged; and one should not be averse to entertaining other reasonable explanations for a source of gunfire. This does not mean that an attorney's speculative questions about triple ricochets off of passing school buses should be pondered unnecessarily. It means that one should not be stubborn about acknowledging that one's reconstruction is an *estimate* of the origin of gunfire. By developing ranges or zones to indicate the origin of gunfire, one is actually stating, "I know where the shot(s) did **NOT** come from." This is often the best one can do with the information given. This process of elimination is frequently crucial to an investigation or trial[9]. It is also easier to truly determine where a bullet did not come from than to know exactly where it originated. This then is the bane of those who would lie about, speculate needlessly, or otherwise pervert the facts of a shooting scene.

There is something inherently wrong with blind "guesstimates" or wild theorizing in the courtroom. The careful analysis of known bullet path parameters (using one fixed and one unfixed target), coupled with accurate measurement and photography, is certainly helpful to the triers of fact.

*   *   *

NOTES

1. Cashman, P.J., "Projectile Entry Angle Determination," **Journal of Forensic Sciences**, Vol. 31, No. 1, Jan. 1986, pp. 86-91.

2. **AFTE Glossary**, 2nd ed., Available Business Forms: Chicago, 1985, p. 136.

3. Steindler, R. A., **The Firearms Dictionary**, Stackpole: Harrisburg, PA, 1970, p. 257.

4. Olson, J., **Encyclopedia of Small Arms**, Winchester Press: Piscataway, NJ, 1985, p. 183.

5. Di Maio, V. J., **Gunshot Wounds**, Elsevier: NY, 1985, p. 91.

6. Geberth, V., **Practical Homicide Investigation**, Elsevier: NY, 1983, p. 21.

7. Garrison, D.H., "Shooting Reconstruction vs Shooting Reenactment," **AFTE Journal**, Vol. 25, No. 1, Jan. 1993, pp. 15-20.

8. Courtney, M. and Hueske, E., "The Use of Hand-held Laser Pointers in the Reconstruction of Events at Crime Scenes," **AFTE Journal**, Vol. 26, No. 3, July 1994, pp. 170-172.

9. Rynearson, J.M. and Chisum, W.J., **Evidence and Crime Scene Reconstruction**, 3rd ed., National Crime Investigation & Training: Redding, CA., 1993, p. 105.

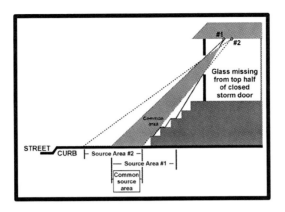

This "source area" determination
tells us that the two shots were not
fired from the street.

Chapter Six

Drive-by Shootings

The drive-by shooting, where a bullet and cartridge case are spewed from a moving vehicle, presents a myriad of problems to the crime scene investigator, as well as the shooting reconstructionist. Often the only scene left is the victim (dead or alive), the spent cartridge cases in the street, or sometimes a witness. Occasionally a trajectory can be established from a shot into a nearby window or wall. More often, the only evidence left is one or more spent cases.

The crime scene investigator needs a general idea of where to look for cartridge cases from a drive-by shooting, how far or near to search, and what the location of recovered cases means. The shooting reconstructionist needs to understand what variables can affect the final location of ejected cases and which speeds, road surfaces, and cartridge types are consistent with a proposed scenario.

For these experiments, fired 12-gauge, .22 Long Rifle, .25 Auto, 9mm Luger, and .45 ACP cartridge cases were dropped, not thrown or tossed, at arm's length from the window (3 to 3 1/2 feet above ground level) of a moving vehicle. Although a couple of cases were lost to storm drains, none were run over by the vehicle's tires. Speed was monitored by speedometer. Measurements were taken from the drop site baseline. Tests were made on smooth pavement, gravel road, and on slopes.

A few things become immediately apparent from a study of the data. First of all, weight does not seem to make an appreciable difference in the final resting place of various caliber cases, at least not within the speed variables of this experiment. Likewise, caliber (case size) seems to make little difference in the results; rimless cases of whatever size end up in the same ranges from the drop point. (Note that, at zero MPH, the minimum curve range begins in the negative; this reflects the fact that if one dropped cases from a stationary position, some would bounce a couple feet backward.)

Secondly, rimmed cases, whether .22 LR or 12-gauge, tend not to travel as far as rimless cases under similar circumstances. Fired shotshells are unwieldy little beasts and, from a rolling-tumbling standpoint, do not travel at all well. Of all the lopsided and un-aerodynamic cartridge cases dropping from cars, the 12-gauge hull tends to stay closest to the original vehicle position. Obviously, the rolling form of a rimmed case is that of a cone, whereas the rolling rimless case forms a cylinder. And cylinders by their nature are better rollers than cones. In crime scenes with a smooth, steep slope, the location of a rimless case may have little to do with the ejection pattern, the actual vehicle position or its speed.

The third obvious conclusion is that, while dirt or gravel roads increase the stopping distance of automobiles, these same surfaces have an enormously retardant effect on ejected cartridge case travel.

A final observation, revealed during these experiments, indicates that the dropping of cases from the left side of a vehicle is not the same as dropping them off the back of a motorcycle, in that almost all cases drift to the left of the vehicle's line-of-travel (or, in a right side ejection, to the right of the vehicle), which is not what one would expect in the hypothetical motorcycle drop. The moving vehicle and/or the wake of its passage through the air seems to shade the area of lateral distribution, and one seldom finds cases to the side opposite the vehicle's ejection side. While this might be a pretty good indicator of the vehicle's lateral position on level surfaces (ie, which traffic lane the car was in at the time of the shooting), this shading effect is lost on inclined roadways, where the excessive rolling of rimless cases can take them far to the left or right of the drop line. Just as rimmed cases tend to tumble and roll shorter linear paths then do rimless cases, they also tend to deviate less laterally from the drop line then the rimless ones. Rimmed cases, therefore, should be better traffic lane indicators than rimless cases. Undisturbed by high winds or meddling passersby, fired shotshells (those poor rollers) should be the best indicators of the position of a vehicle in a drive-by shooting.

A note of caution is in order here, as there are a multitude of imponderable variables that can affect the final resting positions of cartridge cases ejected from a moving automobile. For example, an incline, either up or down, can affect the behavior of the thrown cases. Should an ejected case fly up and temporarily "ride" the roof or trunk of the vehicle, the distances would become distorted.

Any peculiarities in the suspected weapon's ejection pattern, such as extreme height or distance, should be included in the estimation. Of course, the rate-of-fire of a multi-shot incident must be considered, including the common occurrence of some cases ejecting back into the car through an open window. Also common are curbs and rough roadside surfaces (ie, grass parkways, gravel shoulders) that impede the travel of the ejected case. After the shooting, other vehicle traffic or an overly curious crowd can move the cases around and warp the data.

For those who are eyeballing a crime scene on the street, keep in mind that 10 miles-per-hour means that a car or cartridge case is moving at roughly 15 feet-per-second, or about an average car-length per second. Twenty MPH translates to two car-lengths per second, 30 MPH to three, 40 to four, and so on. A cartridge case ejecting very high and spending an inordinate half-second in the air is going to land in a somewhat different spot than the dropped cases cited here. With good on-scene work at the start, these factors can be evaluated at a later time.

No competent shooting reconstructionist would put all his eggs in one basket, nor should he estimate a vehicle position based on the location of a single fired case that has been subject to slope incline, roadway traffic, or any of the other aforementioned imponderables. Two or more ejected case locations, combined with a reasonable evaluation of the imponderable elements, can lead the reconstructionist to a conservative estimate of the drive-by vehicle's position.

Finally, I knew the tests were working when, having lost track of a cartridge case, I returned to the charts of known tumble distances, figured out where the case ought to be located, and then went out and found it based on the test results.

This was, of course, the main goal of the experiment: to find out if tests could provide the scene investigator with a reasonable estimate of where ejected cases should be found and then properly photographed and measured, so that a shooting reconstruction might be successfully completed.

*   *   *

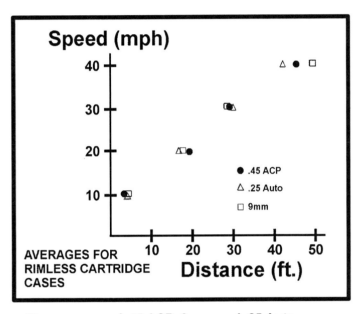

The averages of .45 ACP, 9mm, and .25 Auto
demonstrate that the post-ejection travels of these
rimless cartridge cases are essentially the same.

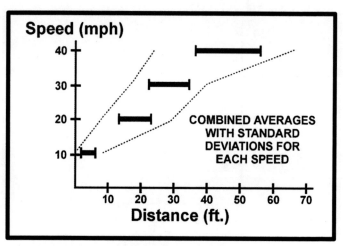

This graph combines the results of .45 ACP, 9mm. and .25 Auto case tests with the standard deviations (horizontal-bars) shown for each speed.

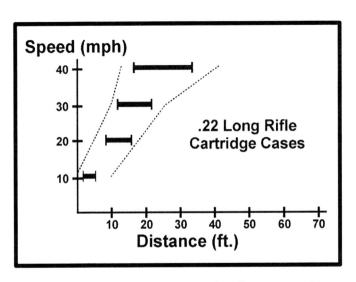

The .22 LR case does not travel well, compared to the rimless cases in this study.

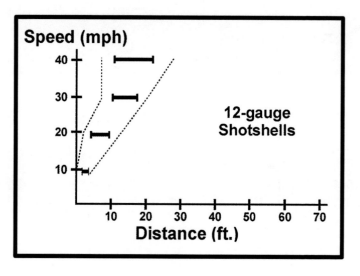

The curve for the 12-gauge shotshell case shows
the limits of this rimmed case's rolling ability.

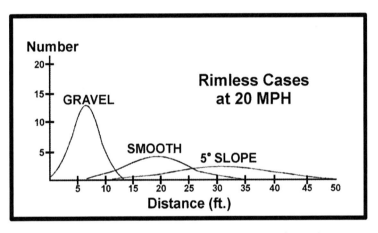

Here the effects of road surface are seen. Gravel
roadways keep ejected cases close to the drop point,
whereas downhill slopes can exaggerate the data.

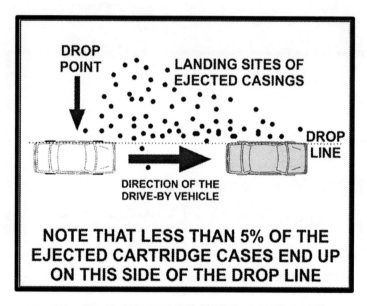

DROP POINT

LANDING SITES OF EJECTED CASINGS

DROP LINE

DIRECTION OF THE DRIVE-BY VEHICLE

NOTE THAT LESS THAN 5% OF THE EJECTED CARTRIDGE CASES END UP ON THIS SIDE OF THE DROP LINE

The locations of ejected casings can often indicate from which side of a vehicle the weapon was fired and which traffic lane the vehicle was in at the time.

Chapter Seven

Vehicle Shootings

Crime scenes involving bullets penetrating or perforating automobile body material must be undertaken with great care so that accurate information can be obtained from the physical evidence. The great varieties of materials comprising the automobile make it even less homogeneous in structure than the human body. Just as a homicide investigation cannot proceed without an close examination of the victim's internal organs, bones, and tissues at autopsy, the reconstruction of a vehicle shooting should not overlook the internal structure of the involved auto body.

In the realm of shooting reconstruction, scenes where bullets strike automobiles are quite common. The interaction of bullets with auto glass has been studied by Cashman and Thornton[1], and Prendergast[2]. Bullet hole formation in sheet steel has been documented by Rathman[3] and Wilber[4]. The dynamics of bullet penetration of auto body sheet metal is the subject of an illustrated study by Nennstiel[5]. The subject of sheet metal ricochet can be found in other research by Rathman[6].

Any line drawn through the schematic of an automobile will intersect numerous and varied materials, including sheet steel, other steel and aluminum members, glass, fiberglass, rubber, plastics, foam padding, linings, weather-strips, sound-deadening materials, card stock, tires, upholstery, and passengers. The variety of materials and their angles of intersection to a bullet's path can result in huge discrepancies in penetration and deflection, even with two entry holes very close together on the vehicle's exterior. Add to this the opening and closing of car doors, windows only partially rolled up, and the often frustrating uncertainty of vehicles that have moved *and* turned both during *and* after a shooting, and one can see that great care must be taken in the examination and analysis of vehicle shootings.

Of all the auto body components, the driver's and passenger's (front) doors are the most commonly encountered and, with their internal locking mechanisms, latches, window systems, mirrors, and various remote controls, are the most complex. Station wagon and van tailgates are often quite elaborate systems also. The rear doors of sedans and cargo doors of vans typically contain much less hardware, both mechanical and electrical[7]. The commonly encountered trunk lid and hood can be simple reinforced sheet metal structures with locks and latching hardware or they can incorporate headlights, tail lights, turn signals, grillwork, and remote control mechanisms; both of these components, however, are the easiest to access when hunting for bullets and tracing bullet paths.

Due to modern automotive styling and aerodynamic design considerations, very few exterior surfaces are perpendicular to the ground level. The bullet entry detail photos, which are typically recorded as scale photographs on roll film or as 1:1 fingerprint camera pictures, are taken with the *lens axis perpendicular to the penetrated surface* (or, if you prefer, with the *film plane parallel to the surface*).

Thus, the bullet hole detail photos are seldom taken at a true horizontal, nor are detail photos of adjacent bullet holes usually taken from the same angle. The context of the entry hole, including its relationship to a true horizon, must be photographed and measured.

One can see that, without these environmental views, the close-up photos alone can be deceptive, especially when one is making measurements and entry angle determinations from scale photographs. It is obviously better to work from the actual hole in the vehicle and best when possible to work on the vehicle at the scene. The other problem with working from photos rather than the vehicle or the scene itself is that information about the position and location of the automobile is not available. At the moment the bullet hole was made, the vehicle may have been swerving sharply, its weight compressing the suspension on one side or its left rear tire may have jumped a curb; the same vehicle at rest would not reflect this tilt. One or more tires may become flat during an incident, again changing the attitude of the auto body surface; elevation and angle measurements must take into account these variables. A height-from-ground-level measurement and in-shoot angle of a bullet hole in a left side door should not be made with a deflated left side tire. Profile photos with a plumb line in view are helpful in correcting any perspective errors. There are dangers in working only with close-up photographs of bullet holes.

One should of course properly record the position and location of the vehicle at the scene, including general view photos, measurements, scale and/or 1:1 photos of the holes, ricochet marks, etc., and, if possible, install and photograph any bullet path probes. All of this should be done *at the scene*, in the context that the bullet holes were made, or at least in the context that they were found. Auto glass should be photographed, measured, and either fixed in place or removed from the vehicle, prior to the vehicle being impounded or released.

The investigation should not stop with the external examination of the involved auto body unit, even if the item was completely perforated. As we have seen, there are numerous internal structures that can affect the path of a perforating bullet. The internal examination is best conducted indoors, where heat, light, tools, power, and soft drinks are available, and only after the appropriate exterior work is completed. It is unwise to start tearing out car parts before the latent print processing and/or bloodstain examinations are finished (or before the search warrant is double-checked). Begin with the right equipment: power screwdrivers (especially Phillips-head), Torx drivers, Allen wrenches, drill, hammer, power saw, drop cloth, mirrors, cameras, scales, plumb lines, gloves, protective eyewear, evidence envelopes, and labels.

Car doors should be disassembled in place, rather than removed from the vehicle. Always begin by spreading out butcher paper or an emergency blanket beneath the work area to catch items falling away during the disassembly. It is a good idea to disconnect the battery cables, as door interiors often contain wiring. Doors are dismantled by removing the interior trim panel's Phillips screws, including arm rests, window crank handles, courtesy light fixtures, and interior handles. Pry the trim panel from the door body and lay it aside. Using a flashlight and dental mirror, examine the interior through access holes in the interior body panel for bullet strike sites and/or fragments. Because automobile doors contain so much hardware, it is important to consider multiple deflection sites and to expect variations in the depths of penetration.

Any defects should be measured from ground level with tires inflated or with the car made level with jacks. It is also necessary to measure these elevations from a fixed reference point or line on the vehicle itself; these dimensions will be independent of elevation variables caused by the car's suspension. Take or photocopy any useful schematics from the owner's manual to help with later trial illustrations.

Measurements should be referenced to the sides and ends of the vehicle (i.e., blood on hood is 17" from front and 23.5" from left side.) To establish the extreme limits of the vehicle's length and width, one can surround the car with taut string attached to four corner tripods, so that the four lines just touch the front and rear bumper tips and the side doors, creating a rectangle. All measurements are then referenced to these lines, as the manufacturer did. The measurements should always be expressed in inches or centimeters (not feet and inches); this is how the manufacturer will have written them in the brochures, repair manuals, replacement part books, and owner's manuals, one or more of which you may later utilize in the preparation of a court exhibit. Keep the door if you can.

If a car window is not already broken, take particular care not to break it, as the fragments will add substantially to your problems in locating bullet fragments. Typically, a shot door is full of shiny glass fragments, including (somewhere!) your shiny metal fragment; you'll need to empty it all out onto your drop sheet and sort through it. This, as anyone who has done it knows, can be a lot of work.

The tools and methods for reaching and recovering bullets and fragments from tight auto body spaces are the same as for any other cramped recovery area. The flex-tube grabbers with plunger handles and rubber-coated three-prong claws are quite handy, although untangled wire hangers with chewing gum or putty or modeling clay applied to a looped end or metal salad tongs with folded and coated spoon-ends will also work. [Serologists would prefer that you soften the gum with sterile water and gloved fingers, rather than actually *chewing* the chewing gum. Older, partially hardened gum works better than fresh-chewed.]

Power screwdrivers, mirrors, and lots of patience are useful, but there are doors, fenders, and quarter panels that will not give up their secrets willingly. There comes a time for electric saws, sledgehammers, and wrecking bars. Staying clear of what you think is the bullet itself and any internal strike sites, make two or three strategic cuts to connect two or more access gaps (preferably from the interior), so that you can fold back a large section of the body panel. This then can be examined, photographed, and measured. For auto body components containing both glass and bullet fragments, you will want to find the lowest point of the item, cut a "drain" hole in the interior or underside, and then sweep (with a probe tip) all the pieces toward the hole.

Practice, as always, helps immensely. Take time to visit a police impound lot or junkyard to look at the insides of an auto body (burned cars are good for this). You'll find that 1973 Chevrolet Novas, 1983 Nissan Maximas, and 1993 Ford F-150 pickups are quite different in the way they receive gunfire. If at all possible, find a junked car, create holes in it from a variety of weapons, and then autopsy the automobile with electric saws, mirrors, and chewing gum to find all the bullet paths and jacket fragments. Part of the training of all crime scene technicians and firearm examiners should include the detailed dissection, measurement, and photography of at least one shot-up car.

*   *   *

NOTES

1. Thornton, J.I. and Cashman, P.J., "The Effect of Tempered Glass on Bullet Trajectory," **Journal of Forensic Sciences**, Vol. 31, No. 2, April 1986, pp. 743-746.

2. Prendergast, J.M., "Determination of Bullet Impact Position from the Examination of Fractured Automobile Safety Glass," **Association of Firearm & Tool Mark Examiners Journal**, Vol. 26, No. 2, April 1994, pp. 107-118.

3. Rathman, G.A., "The Effects of Material Hardness on the Appearance of Bullet Impact Damage," **AFTE Journal**, Vol. 20, No. 3, July 1988, pp. 300-305.

4. Wilber, C., **Ballistics Science for the Law Enforcement Officer**, Charles Thomas: Springfield, IL, 1977.

5. Nennstiel, R., "Forensic Aspects of Bullet Penetration of Thin Metal Sheets," **AFTE Journal**, Vol. 18, No. 2, April 1986, pp. 18-48.

6. Rathman, G.A., "Bullet Ricochet and Associated Phenomena," **AFTE Journal**, Vol. 19, No. 4, Oct. 1987, pp. 374-381.

7. Sargent, R.L., **Chilton's Mechanic's Handbook Volume 3: Auto Body Sheet Metal Repair**, Chilton Books: Radnor, PA, 1981, p. 151.

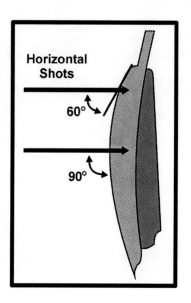

Care must be taken in measuring angles from the curved surfaces of auto bodies.

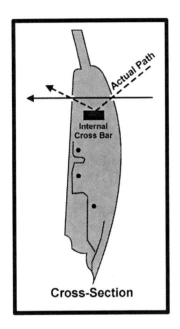

Cross-Section

Objects within a car
door can change the
angle of a shot.
Simply connecting the
outside holes with a
probe may not be
enough.

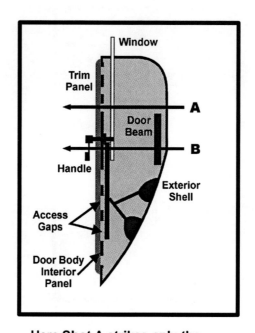

Here Shot A strikes only the outer shell of the door and the trim panel, whereas Shot B encounters a variety of internal hardware in its path.

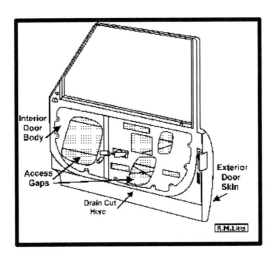

Interior Door Body

Access Gaps

Drain Cut Here

Exterior Door Skin

R.M.Litts

This shows the inner shell of the door body. Mirrors, flashlights, and a variety of tools are useful for exploring auto bodies.

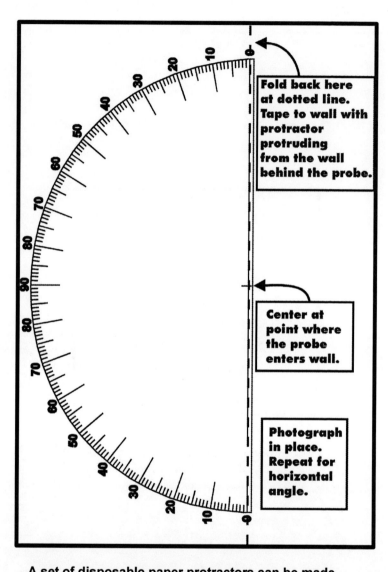

Fold back here at dotted line. Tape to wall with protractor protruding from the wall behind the probe.

Center at point where the probe enters wall.

Photograph in place. Repeat for horizontal angle.

A set of disposable paper protractors can be made on a copy machine. These can be taped to a probed surface and photographed in place.

Chapter Eight

Road Structure as it Affects Bullet Path Angles in Vehicle Shootings

When working on crime scene where shots are fired into a vehicle, whether parked or moving, it will be valuable to the investigator to know how much of the in-shoot angle is the result of the roadway design and how much is the product of the shooter's position. When one is examining a vehicle in an evidence garage far from the scene, working on a shot vehicle that has moved from the crime scene, or—worse case scenario—working from photographs only, one is missing the environmental context in which the vehicle was shot, and this can be fatal to an analysis. The floors of evidence garages are usually flat; roadways are often not level. We are not talking here about the slopes and inclines of hilly streets, which are usually obvious. Here we will address the so-called *cross-slope*, that variation in level across the width of a roadway.

As a driver the most obvious cross-slope angle one notices is the *bank*. A banked curve is lower on the inside and higher on the outside to help keep higher speed vehicles from sliding off the road. Civil engineers call this *superelevation*, which is defined as the difference between the height of the road's outside edge and the road's inside edge. The faster the anticipated traffic on the curved section of roadway, the higher the superelevation. Raceways and automotive test tracks feature extreme examples of curve banking. The less obvious examples of superelevation are those of freeway curves. One can notice the advantages of banking when one takes a curve too fast or when one is driving on rain, snow, or ice; the tilt of the roadway helps the car stay on its course. To see the superelevation, one only needs to view it on foot or look directly out the side windows while passing through the curve.

The second, much less obvious, yet much more common, manifestation of cross-slope is the *crown*, sometimes called *camber*. A crown is the rise in the middle of a road that facilitates drainage. Crowned roadways are present to some extent in almost all city streets and, thus, would most frequently affect the vehicle shooting scene. As a convexity, the crown is not so noticeable in the center (the traffic lanes) but becomes more profound at the road's edges, sometimes a shoulder, but usually a curb. For vehicle shootings that occur by the curb, the tilt of a crowned street can alter the angle of in-shoots, such that they not longer make sense on a level evidence garage floor. While the cross-slope angle of a crowned roadway rarely exceeds about six degrees, this can have a great effect on an estimate of shooter's position. Worn and sunken pavement, deep gutters, and high curbs can further confound the reconstruction of bullet paths. The vehicle can be removed from the scene for processing and analysis, but the reconstructionist should not form conclusions without the context of the involved roadway.

Recognizing that roadway cross-slope can affect a vehicle's level and, thus, the in-shoot angles of bullet paths through the vehicle, one must be able to measure the cross-slope angle. Engineers measure such slopes as *grade*, the rise or fall in feet per foot of horizontal distance, or *percent grade*, the rise or fall in feet per 100 feet of horizontal distance. For the purpose of crime scene measurement, a simple vertical angle measurement is all that is needed. This is most easily accomplished by laying an inclinometer on a smooth section of the slope in question. For those who do not have an inclinometer as part of their crime scene processing equipment, the same angles can be measured using a clipboard, a ruler with centered holes in it, and a pencil.

Important points to remember are that the cross-slope on one side of the roadway may different from that of the opposite side; slope is not consistent the full length of a street or block; gutters and dropped road shoulders can greatly increase the tilt of a vehicle; and clipboard measurements should not be made on very rough (i.e., gravel) surfaces. Good on-scene photographs, including vehicle end-views taken with a normal focal length (not wide angle) lens, can help in establishing the vehicle tilt. By recording the roadway structure with measurement and photography, the investigator can save time and wasted effort in a later vehicle shooting reconstruction.

* * *

Suggested Reading

Baker, J. S., **Traffic Accident Investigation Manual**, 2nd. ed., (Northwestern University: Evanston, IL), 1975.

The Civil Engineering Handbook, W. F. Chen, editor-in-chief, (CRC Press: Boca Raton, FL), 1995.

Gilson, G., **Concrete Flatwork Manual**, (Craftsman Book Company: Carlsbad, CA), 1982.

Lindberg, M.R., **Civil Engineering Reference Manual**, 6th ed., (Professional Publications: Belmont, CA), 1992.

Means Illustrated Construction Dictionary, Smit, K. and H. Chandler, eds., (R.S. Means: Kingston, MA), 1991.

Overman, M., **Roads, Bridges, and Tunnels: Modern Approaches to Road Engineering**, (Doubleday: NY), 1968.

This photo shows the dramatic effect that a road's crown can have on vehicle levels.

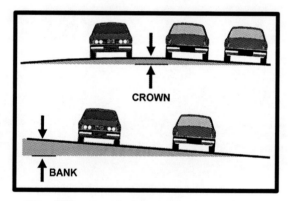

The difference between a crowned
street and a banked roadway.

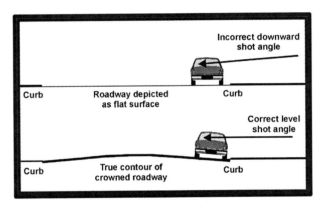

Failing to take into account the tilting
effect of a road's crown can lead to errors
in shot angle estimates.

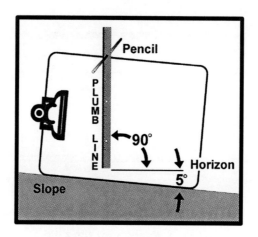

**Suspending a ruler from a pencil
can create a plumb line for
simple road slope measurement.**

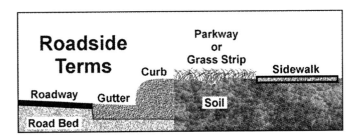

Roadside Terms

Roadway · Gutter · Curb · Parkway or Grass Strip · Sidewalk · Soil · Road Bed

These are the basic parts of curb work.

Chapter Nine

Problems with Glass

The glass usually encountered at shooting crime scenes is of three kinds: flat glass, tempered glass, and laminated glass. Each has its own characteristics and uses. Each responds to gunfire in different ways. Neither the role of glass as trace evidence nor its laboratory analysis will be discussed. Here we are interested in the on-scene examination of bullet defects in windows.

The glass commonly used in building windows, mirrors, and furniture cabinets is called *flat glass*. Flat glass is sometimes called *sheet glass*, *plate glass*, or *float glass*, depending on the manufacturing process. Sheet glass is made with rollers; plate glass, usually thicker, is also made with rollers but is highly polished afterward, a more expensive process. Float glass is made by floating sheets of molten glass across pools of molten tin, a less expensive process that results in a very smooth and very clear glass. All types of flat glass are produced in the form of flat sheets and react to bullet impact similarly. Standard household windows are sheet glass. Heavy storefront windows and display cases are often made of plate glass or float glass, which offer a cleaner surface and clearer view. Broken plate glass produces large, jagged, and very sharp-edged fragments and is nasty stuff for both burglars and crime scene workers. Wire-reinforced glass is simply standard flat glass with a wire netting embedded in the glass; wired glass cannot be tempered.

The second type of glass of interest to the shooting investigator is *tempered glass*. Also known as *safety glass*, *tempered glass* is glass that has been formed, then reheated, and cooled rapidly. There are also chemical processes that use molten salt for the tempering of glass. Tempered safety glass can be up to five times as strong as a similar piece of untempered glass. Its most favorable characteristics are its strength and the way it breaks, disintegrating into small, dull-edged fragments. These attributes make tempered glass ideal for such things as the windows of automobiles and for bathroom shower doors. Tempered glass windows must be completely formed to their final shape before tempering, because any later cutting or shaping will shatter them.

The third glass type is *laminated glass*. Used in car windshields, very large storefront windows, and some glass security doors, laminated glass is made by sandwiching plastic sheeting between two layers of glass. With sufficient impact, the glass breaks, but the fragments are held in place by the plastic layer and do not create dangerous flying shards. Laminated glass is standard material for all American-made automobile windshields; European cars are made with tempered glass in all windows, including the windshield. Bullet-resistant windows often utilize multiple layers of glass and plastic. The large tinted windows in commercial structures are usually laminates.

Other materials used for windows, such as Plexiglas (acrylic sheet) and Lexan (polycarbonate sheet), are plastics and not glass at all. They do not behave like glass when struck by a projectile and, thus, should not be subjected to the same examination. On the other hand, fiberglass, which really is made from glass and is used to reinforce plastics in auto bodies and some building materials, does *not* behave like glass either.

Bullets obviously can perforate glass. The size of the hole left has little meaning in relation to the size of the projectile making it. Given the right striking angle or a slow enough speed, a projectile can be deflected from a window, leaving behind anything from a scratch to a chunk-out. Projectiles can also presumably penetrate a glass surface and become lodged in the material, although the author has only seen this with laminated glass. A bullet can also *spall* a glass pane, which means its strikes the glass without fully perforating and, in doing so, imparts enough energy to the surface that the side opposite the impact site chips or flakes off. A spall can occur on other brittle surfaces, such as masonry and reinforced walls in bomb-shelter buildings.

In its passage through a window, a bullet creates ever-widened lines of force, so that the entry side is small and the exit side is larger. This *cone effect* is most easily seen in strikes by air-gun pellets or BBs, where the surrounding glass is not greatly changed by the impact. Spalls also exhibit the cone effect, the chipped off area on the opposite side of the glass being larger than the impact site. Bullet paths perpendicular to the glass tend to leave symmetrical cones; angled shots make asymmetrical cones. With thick glass, the cone effect can be pronounced and may be photographed. With thinner panes and tempered glass, the cone is either too small to see or has collapsed with the rest of the pane. To demonstrate the cone, one could make a cast of the defect or simply apply fingerprint powder to the entry and the exit and make tape lifts of their outlines. Glass defects of any kind are more easily photographed by dulling them with steam (warm breath on a cold window) or print powder.

The first cracks to form in a window upon a projectile strike are the *radial fractures*, those that start from the center of the impact site and radiate away. Radial fractures, however, begin forming on the side **opposite** the impact, where the glass is stretching away from the force. If one were to slowly press one's finger into a piece of cloth, one can see that the fibers opposite the finger stretch apart first, while the threads on the finger side are compressed. Radial fractures may extend to the edges of the glass, depending on the force of the strike and the size of the window. In all three types of glass discussed here, radial fractures can be traced back to their focal origin, even if the actual strike site has fallen away. Radial fractures in tempered safety glass, however, extend uniformly for a distance, but then *craze*, as the tempered glass fragmentation begins, and are no longer meaningful to the determination of an impact site. Radial fractures produced in windows will not cross pre-existing radial fractures. This is useful when more than one projectile strikes a single pane of glass or when one defect is made from the interior and one from the exterior. The radial fractures from the second impact will not cross the radial fractures from the first impact. Laminated glass with its two layers can make radial fracture analysis unreliable.

While the glass is bending in the direction of the force, the rest of the window is holding back. Secondary breaks begin to form in circles around the strike site and on the same side as the strike. These circular cracks, called *concentric fractures* (or sometimes *spiral cracks*), occur as the remainder of the window refuses to stretch any further. Unlike radial fractures, concentric fractures do not really point to anything and can be caused by the secondary collapse of the pane. The formation of concentric fractures is dependent on the size of the pane and how rigidly it is supported in its frame. Some windows may exhibit no concentric fracturing at all.

The edge (cross-section) of a glass fracture shows curved lines called *stress marks*, which parallel one side of the glass but curve to a right angle as they meet the other side of the glass. Even if much of the glass has fallen out of a window, one only needs to find a piece and look at the stress marks on the edge of a **radial** fracture. The stress lines will curve to a right angle against one side of the glass; in a radial fracture, this is the reverse side from which the force was applied. The importance of understanding how and where both radial and concentric fractures are formed is in examining their edges and knowing the 3-R Rule. The 3-R Rule goes something like this:

Radial fractures form Right angles on the Reverse side of the impact.

And, just to confuse things more, with concentric fractures it's just the opposite (that is, *concentric fractures form right angles on the same side as the impact*). If one forgets the 3-R Rule in the field, one should mark a large fragment ("R" for *radial*, "C" for *concentric*, "INT" for *interior*, and "EXT" for *exterior*) and bring it back to headquarters to check the rule book or have the piece looked at by someone with a better memory. It is better to examine radial fractures only, as these can be directly attributed to the impact site and not some secondary cracking.

Tempered glass, with its propensity to craze and collapse, is usually impossible to reassemble from fragments. However, while still in place the stronger glass may show bending in the direction of the force. Laminated glass will do this, too, and will sometimes form a concave cup in the plastic inner layer where the bullet struck and stretched the plastic. As mentioned earlier, radial fractures will not cross other radial fractures that are already present on flat and tempered glass. This, plus the crazing effect of safety glass fractures, means that an irregularly shaped hole, where other pieces are missing near an existing the bullet hole, could in fact be a second bullet impact site.

Whether glass fragments fall to the interior or exterior of a broken window is due to a number of factors and should not be given too much significance. Simply by virtue of their fracture formation, radial fractures produce glass fragments in the back side and concentric fractures break out pieces on the front side of a struck window. A glass pane backed by a taut curtain or metal grillwork will drop most of its fragments on the exterior even when broken from the exterior. A hole shot low into a window may propel glass fragments into a room, but the remainder of the pane above it may collapse and fall to either side or both inside and out. Angled panes, such as those in the rear windows of cars, will collapse downward and apparently inward, even when shot from the inside. Any foot traffic or movement of a broken glass door spreads the fragments, making them useless for analysis.

Other types of fragment distribution can be very helpful in reconstructing a bullet path. Very fine particulate glass spray can be found on door frames, window sills, car seat headrests, and other nearby items. For angled shots at windows, this spray pattern may appear as a V-pattern with its point aiming back at the strike site. Once the glass dust is cleared away, the true outline of the deflection defect can be seen as a "comet" shaped gouge. Research by Chisum, Rynearson, and others indicates that the longest portion of the comet's tail is a direct result of the bullet's spin and, thus, the direction of twist of the rifled barrel that fired that bullet. A defect comet with a longer tail on the left side means the weapon that fired it has rifling with a left hand twist. In spalls, the fragments chipped from the struck side have little velocity, whereas the spalled fragments from the back side (following the line of force) are sometimes propelled into human flesh and upholstery. Manufacturers of bullet-resistant windows have learned to coat or seal the interior of laminates so that people are not injured or killed by spalled glass fragments on the protected side.

When shots are fired into the tempered windows of moving vehicles, the glass drop sites can be important. The first sign of automobile glass on a roadway should be noted, measured, and photographed. The dropping fragments are moving at the same speed and direction as the vehicle from which they fell, so the drop site is not exactly the shooting site. Tempered safety glass may not always collapse immediately, nor will a whole pane necessarily drop all at the same time. A side window may be perforated and weakened by a shot but not drop until the car hits the next bump or pothole. One should remember that all subsequent traffic in an eastbound traffic lane will tend to carry dropped glass fragments further eastward. Glass drop sites, therefore, should only be used as a guide in estimating where a vehicle shooting occurred. They can, however, be very useful starting points in locating one's crime scene.

One should take the time to examine and practice photographing the defects in glass that one encounters at non-critical scenes (vandalism, property crimes, etc.), so that one can correctly interpret the glass breakage evidence at more important scenes.

* * *

Suggested Reading

De Forest, P. R., Gaensslen, R. E., and H. C. Lee, **Forensic Science: An Introduction to Criminalistics**, (McGraw-Hill: NY), pp. 170-171.

Garrison, D. H., "A Template for Reconstructing the Center-of-Impact in Broken Windows," **MAFS Newsletter**, Oct 1990, pp. 38-40.

Gieszl, R., "Stabilization of Glass Fractures," **AFTE Journal**, Vol. 22, No. 4, Oct. 1990, p. 440.

Maxey, R.R., "Fracture Analysis of Tempered Glass," **AFTE Journal**, Vol. 15, No. 2, April 1983, pp. 114-116.

Omilion, P.M., "The Effects of Window Glass on Shotgun Pellets Patterns," **AFTE Journal**, Vol. 11, No. 4, Oct. 1979, pp. 54-57.

Prendergast, J.M., "Determination of Bullet Impact Position from the Examination of Fractured Automobile Glass," **AFTE Journal**, Vol. 26, No. 2, April 1994, pp. 107-118.

Rathman, G.A., "Bullet Impact Damage and Trajectory Through Auto Glass," **AFTE Journal**, Vol. 25, No. 2, April 1993, pp. 79-86.

Rynearson, J. M., and W. J. Chisum, **Evidence and Crime Scene Reconstruction**, 3rd. ed., (National Crime Investigation & Training: Redding, CA), pp. 117-119.

Saferstein, R., **Forensic Science Handbook**, (Prentise-Hall: Englewood Cliffs, NJ), pp. 146-150 and 168-173.

Smith, L.L., "Bullet Holes in Glass," reprinted **AFTE Newsletter**, No. 10, Oct. 1970, pp. 14-15.

Thornton, J.I. and Cashman, P.J., "The Effect of Tempered Glass on Bullet Trajectory," **Journal of Forensic Sciences**, JFSCA, Vol. 31, No. 2, April 1986, pp. 743-746.

Thornton, J.I. and Cashman, P.J., "Glass Fracture Mechanism—A Rethinking," **Journal of Forensic Sciences**, JFSCA, Vol. 31, No. 3, July 1986, pp. 818-824.

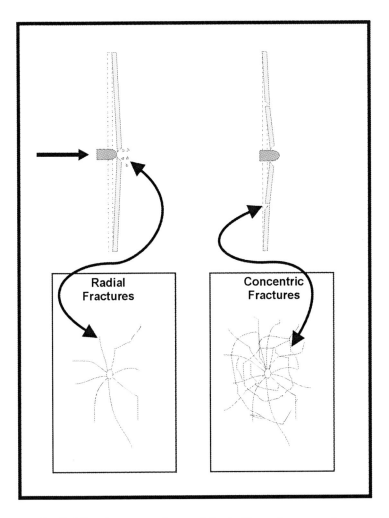

Radial Fractures

Concentric Fractures

Radial fractures are formed first. No subsequent fracture lines will cross these pre-existing cracks.

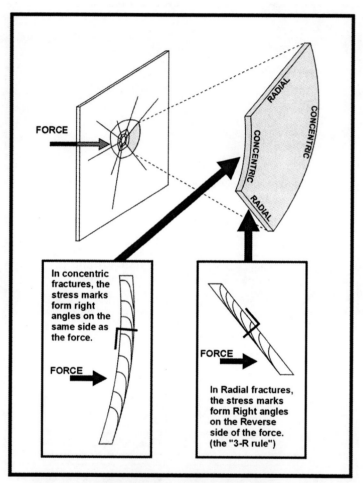

FORCE

RADIAL
CONCENTRIC
CONCENTRIC
RADIAL

In concentric fractures, the stress marks form right angles on the same side as the force.

FORCE

FORCE

In Radial fractures, the stress marks form Right angles on the Reverse side of the force. (the "3-R rule")

This is the 3-R Rule illustrated. It is often hard to see and always difficult to photograph.

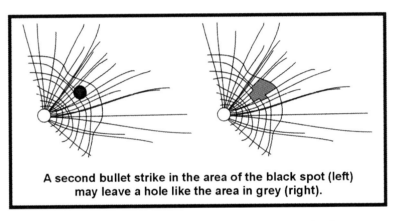

A second bullet strike in the area of the black spot (left)
may leave a hole like the area in grey (right).

In safety glass, a second bullet hole may only look
like a dropped out section of the previous fracture.

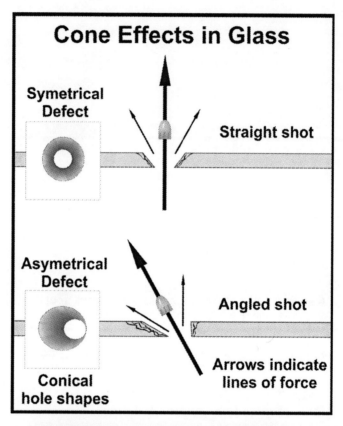

Cone Effects in Glass

Symetrical Defect

Straight shot

Asymetrical Defect

Angled shot

Conical hole shapes

Arrows indicate lines of force

An angled shot cannot leave a symmetrical cone. In the lower example, it may only be possible to describe the angle as right-to-left, although that in itself eliminates all other directions.

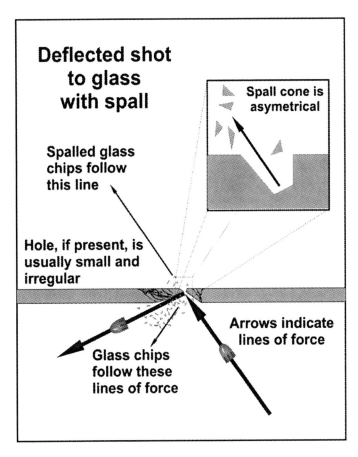

Deflected shot to glass with spall

Spall cone is asymetrical

Spalled glass chips follow this line

Hole, if present, is usually small and irregular

Arrows indicate lines of force

Glass chips follow these lines of force

Spalls are rare phenomena, but are frequently mistaken for true perforations.

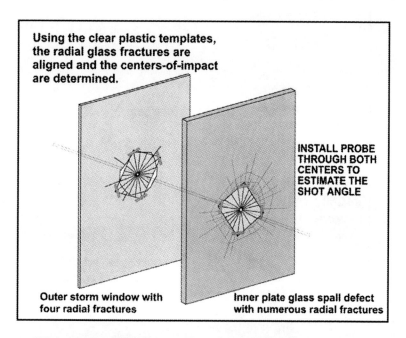

Using the clear plastic templates, the radial glass fractures are aligned and the centers-of-impact are determined.

INSTALL PROBE THROUGH BOTH CENTERS TO ESTIMATE THE SHOT ANGLE

Outer storm window with four radial fractures

Inner plate glass spall defect with numerous radial fractures

Without aligning the centers of the radial fractures, one cannot determine accurately the shot angle.

Chapter Ten

Angled Shot Pellet Patterns

Crime scene work on the street is often a quick and dirty business. There just isn't a lot of time for trigonometry, biochemistry, or What-if? second-guessing. The shootings are usually no-gun investigations with no answers and few cooperative witnesses. Your photos have to come out, your sketches must make sense, and your evidence receipts have to match number and letter to your report. . .or else! And it all has to be done right the first time, right now, hurry up, there's another call waiting, let's get going! With this in mind, let's address the problem of how to record and interpret angled shotgun blasts fired into walls (doors, cars, etc.) in a quick and not so dirty way.

The flying charge of shot, as we know, describes a gradually expanding cone shape. Experiments have shown, however, that the angle formed by the widening cone over the short span of its collision with a wall is so small as to be negligible for measuring purposes. Thus, the flying shot charge may be considered a straight-sided cylinder instead of the ever-widening cone. It has also been pointed out that the more acute the angle of the blast to the flat wall, the more accurate are calculations based on measurements of the ellipse.[1] Simply put, the more elongated the ellipse, the better it works.

One of the most common examples of an angled intersection between a cylinder and a plane is a roof chimney pipe protruding from a pitched roof. An ellipse has to be cut in the angled roof to accommodate the round chimney. The narrow aspect (Minor Axis) of this elliptical hole is the same size as the chimney's diameter. The long aspect (Major Axis) of the hole allows the pipe to pass through at an angle. If we had only a hole in the roof, we could figure out the chimney diameter from the ellipse's narrow aspect and could draw on paper the angle at which this chimney would fit into the long aspect of the elliptical hole.

With an angled shot pattern on a wall, we have the roof hole (pattern) without the chimney pipe (direction of the flying shot charge). By measuring the Minor Axis of the pattern—and this measuring is by far the most important part of the examination—we know the width of the pattern as if it had struck the wall straight-on at a right angle. Knowing the Major Axis of the pattern on the wall and the width of the thrown shot charge, we can make a scale drawing of the pattern, fitting the cylinder size into the ellipse size, and finding the angle at which they come together (the angle of intersection). Furthermore, this can be accomplished with relative ease on a clipboard at the crime scene. . .without trigonometry!

The first thing, of course, is the photography. While one's first observations and photographs of an angled shot pattern may only be a rough estimation of the shooter's position, good scene photos must be taken. A basic outline might include the following steps:

A.) Photograph the environment of the pellet pattern, noting witness views, sight obstructions, and possible intermediate targets.[2]

B.) Make perpendicular scale photographs of the pattern with a marker for vertical orientation.[3]

C.) Locate the pattern by measurement on the scene sketch and elevation diagram. Measure the Major Axis (usually horizontal width) and the Minor Axis (usually height), discounting obvious fliers.[4]

D.) Using chalk, marker, or pieces of tape, mark the outline of the pattern and photograph this again from area views.

E.) Using the Minor Axis measurement as the pattern's true width, estimate the weapon-to-target distance by the old rule of thumb of 1" pattern spread = 1 yd. muzzle-to-target distance.[5] Keep in mind any vertical elongation of the ellipse which might indicate a shooter's position significantly above or below the level of the pattern.[6]

F.) Find the approximate shot angle. Looking through your camera lens, position yourself at a spot where the previously marked ellipse appears as a true circle.[7] Remember, this probably won't be at your eye level. (This can make hunting for wads and/or casings much easier.)

G.) Mark the spot and photograph a reverse view of it from the angled pellet pattern on the wall. Photograph area views to include both the pattern and the aforementioned spot. These photos should include a generous area behind the approximated shooter's position in the event that your range estimate is too short.

You may want to do more, like cutting down the wall, door, etc. and taking it with you, but these are the basic steps. An instant photo of the area view in Step G may aid investigators, especially if a human figure is placed at the shooter's approximated position.[8]

You may even want to do the math (or analytic geometry), even if it's only to confirm the information you've already learned from the on-scene work.

Once the measurements of the elliptical pellet pattern have been recorded, you can make a scale drawing and estimate the angle of intersection, as follows, on a standard notebook sheet. This method makes for less "eyeballing" guesswork and more systematic and reasoned scene work.

* * *

NOTES

1. Lattig, K. "The Determination of the Angle of Intersection of a Shot Pellet Charge with a Flat Surface," **AFTE Journal**, Vol. 14, No. 3, July 1982, pp. 13-17.

2. Breitenecker, R., and Senior, W., "Shotgun Patterns I: An Experimental Study on the Influence of Intermediate Targets," **Journal of Forensic Sciences**, Vol. 12, No. 2, April 1967, pp. 193-204.

3. Fisher, B., **Techniques of Crime Scene Investigation**, 5th ed., CRC Press: Boca Raton, FL, 1993.

4. Lattig, K.

5. Dillon, J., "A Protocol for Shot Pattern Examinations in Muzzle-to-target Distance Determination," **AFTE Journal**, Vol. 23, No. 1, Jan. 1991, pp. 511-21.

6. *The inch-pattern-spread-equals-yard-shotgun-range is a useful, if primitive, tool. Obviously, there are differences in shotguns, shotshells, and chokes, but one seldom has these specifics at the initial crime scene, nor is there time to go off and fire a series of test shots. If you knew the weapon's exact make, model, choke, and ammunition, you'd already have the crime gun in hand. So, yes, the inch-yard rule-of-thumb is a valid device for scene work and, if it's all you ever get, it becomes a useful approximating tool for the courtroom. You make do with the cards you are dealt, so long as everybody understands the terms "fair" and "accurate," and recognizes the answer as an estimate.*

7. *If you shine a flashlight on an angled wall while holding it up close to one open eye, you'll notice that the spot on the wall appears circular, even though you know that it forms an ellipse on the plane of the wall. This is how the shotgun muzzle "sees" the shot pattern on the angled surface. If you can find and photograph the point from which a markedly elliptical shot pattern appears circular, you're getting warm in finding*

the muzzle's vantage point and the ballpark of the shooter's position, which is all you may ever get. Telephoto views from a distance make finding the vantage point much clearer.

8. Ohara, C., **Fundamentals of Criminal Investigation**, 2nd ed., Thomas: Springfield, IL, 1972.

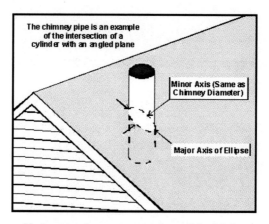

The chimney pipe is an example
of the intersection of a
cylinder with an angled plane

Minor Axis (Same as
Chimney Diameter)

Major Axis of Ellipse

**Not every juror remembers his high
school geometry, but most of them
know what a chimney looks like.**

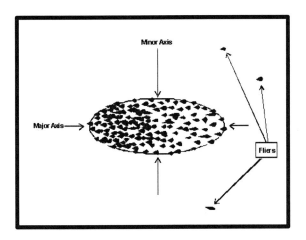

Fliers are not always this obvious, but they should not be considered part of the pattern dimensions.

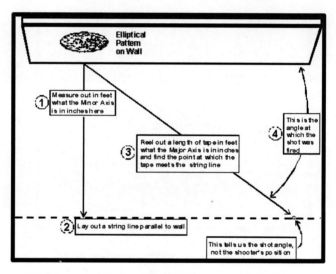

Elliptical Pattern on Wall

① Measure out in feet what the Minor Axis is in inches here

② Lay out a string line parallel to wall

③ Reel out a length of tape in feet what the Major Axis is in inches and find the point at which the tape meets the string line

④ This is the angle at which the shot was fired

This tells us the shot angle, not the shooter's position

This is a simpler method, if you can't do the math.

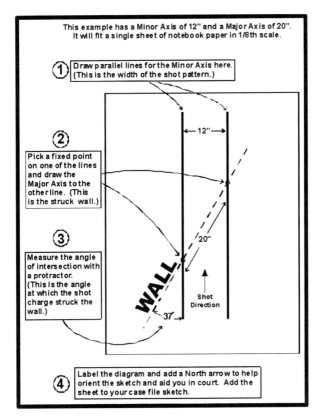

This example has a Minor Axis of 12" and a Major Axis of 20".
It will fit a single sheet of notebook paper in 1/8th scale.

(1) Draw parallel lines for the Minor Axis here.
(This is the width of the shot pattern.)

(2) Pick a fixed point on one of the lines and draw the Major Axis to the other line. (This is the struck wall.)

← 12" →

(3) Measure the angle of intersection with a protractor. (This is the angle at which the shot charge struck the wall.)

20"

WALL

37°

Shot Direction

(4) Label the diagram and add a North arrow to help orient the sketch and aid you in court. Add the sheet to your case file sketch.

This hand-drawn method works well at the scene and can make a clear and understandable courtroom exhibit.

Chapter Eleven

Searching Scenes and Backdrops

In the search of a shooting crime scene one should avoid the tunnel vision that causes one to see only the immediate area or consider only the evidence already located by on-scene personnel. Keep in mind that just because a witness, even a police witness, *heard* two shots doesn't mean there are two casings or *any* casings to be found, nor does it mean that more than two casings might be found. Just because someone found an old .22 cartridge case doesn't mean it is necessarily involved in the incident or that other casings should not be sought. If a car is hit by a bullet from a running gun battle, chances are good that the buildings around the car have also sustained damage. Even though shots from a drive-by shooting were fired at 306 ABC Street doesn't mean that one can't examine the walls, porches, fences, and garages at 302, 304, 308, and 310 ABC Street.

In a multi-shot incident, the one bullet that struck down the victim may be too deformed to be useful as evidence, but the bullet that missed him and lodged in a nearby utility pole may be in great shape for identification. At times, with living gunshot victims, an emergency room doctor elects not to surgically remove the projectile, and the bullet that missed becomes the only identifiable evidence.

If, as a crime scene investigator, one finds several inactive and restless street officers wandering about the scene, one can assign these people the job of searching the backdrop of the target. The backdrop can be described as any object downrange beyond what is thought to be the intended target. Shooting scenes frequently show deflection defects (ricochet marks) in intermediate targets (items hit by a bullet before it comes to rest) and other marks on the backdrop. If one finds a deflection point in either type of site, the size, shape, depth, and angle should be properly recorded by photography and measurement, and the search should continue for secondary and tertiary deflection sites.

On daylight scenes one can establish exactly what the backdrop is by standing at the estimated shooter's position and taking an instant photograph in the direction of the shooting. All the surfaces that appear in the resulting picture (including all those buildings, signs, and poles in the background) can then be used as a guide by the backdrop searchers. At nighttime scenes, a flashlight or vehicle spotlight can be aimed around the approximate field-of-fire; all of the illuminated surfaces can then be examined. If the beam of light leaks between two houses to illuminate a tree or roof edge in the next city block, someone should be sent over to check out these backdrop surfaces. Many special weapons team members and police officers with an infantry background understand the concept of "fields of fire" (those areas that can be reached by gunfire from a given shooter's position) and can apply the idea to scene searching.

When one finds a single defect or deflection point, one should search for others. Such a discovery should not lull the searcher into thinking that he or she has found the one and only bullet hole, but should indicate that the searcher is "getting warm" in the hunt for other defects. The scene investigation should not be sidetracked by the input of neighbors, who claim that a defect found on their property is old or is not a projectile defect at all. These sites need to be examined by a competent investigator to determine if they appear to be caused by gunfire and are consistent with the rest of the evidence.

Area vehicles should be secured until the scene work is done. A vehicle parked near a shooting scene, like any other fixed structure, creates a shadow effect on the scene's backdrop. Projectile evidence from a given shooter's position should not be found in the shadowed area of the backdrop. Likewise, the introduction of vehicles into the scene after the shooting should be limited as much as possible. These are crime scene preservation issues and, therefore, should be addressed early in the investigation. This truck was here, that bus was over there, and someone took off in a cab that was parked on the corner; these facts need to be established right away, as they can cause needless work later for the crime scene team. Keeping in mind that the ground and the pavement are also part of a shooting scene's backdrop, one must remember to search the area under every police, fire, and EMS vehicle that has entered the scene. Evidence from shooting scenes can be quite small (shotgun pellets, bullet jacket fragments, etc.), and it's easy to park a vehicle, even a crime scene truck, on top of them.

One point often overlooked in the search of a shooting crime scene is the backdrop of the *shooter's* position. If Subject A is shooting to the west at Subject B, it is not unheard-of that Subject B may also be firing back to the east at Subject A. Furthermore, the casings found around Subject B's dead body may not be from the weapon that shot him, but may have been ejected by the weapons that Subject B's friends were firing back at Subject A. It's always important to sift through the known facts with a cautious and skeptical eye.

As these examples show, it is important to examine the overall environment of a shooting scene to establish its limits and its evidentiary potential. The first story one hears and the small area around the bloodstain may not reveal the whole incident. An thorough search of the shooting scene's backdrop does not always yield useful evidence but, as we know, that which is not searched for is not found.

This is an example of an embedded bullet. Typical of bullets found in distant backdrops, it lacked the energy to fully penetrate the wooden wall. This particular item was found half a block from the homicide scene.

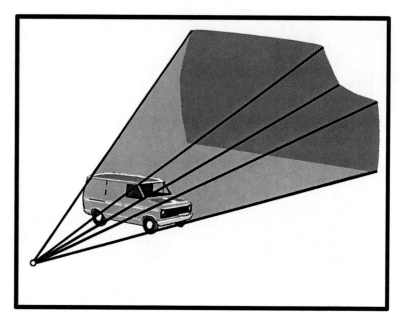

Vehicles create areas of shadow, where bullets cannot go. It is important that vehicles remain in their places at the scene of a shooting. Note that the right side of this vehicle qualifies as a backdrop area where bullets may be found.

The backdrop of this shooting scene includes the two buildings, the vehicle, and whatever a bullet can reach between the buildings. All of these areas may contain additional items of evidence.

Chapter Twelve

Matters of Intent

Just because a shot was fired, and just because someone was injured or died as a result of the shooting, and just because a shooting reconstruction was completed...this does **not** mean that the expert can render an opinion about the intent behind the bullet thus fired.

While many an attorney, whether prosecution or defense, wants to "prove" the intent or lack thereof to a jury, and sometimes tries to use a expert witness to accomplish that end, this does not mean that the shooting reconstruction expert has any scientific basis whatsoever to state an opinion as to what was or was not the *intention* of the shooter at the moment of the shooting. Intent, after all, is usually an "ultimate issue" and, thus, the purview of the jury, the finders of fact, and cannot properly be addressed by the expert.[1]

Only psychiatrists and psychologists, those paragons of consistently precise opinion and sound experimental scientific integrity, are capable of tackling the issue of intent, often termed "the ability or lack thereof to form the specific intent to commit the crime in question" or words to that effect. And what person endowed with scientific thought would want to wade into the quagmire of psychiatric expert testimony anyway?

In shooting reconstruction, as with all reconstruction, the practitioner's work tries to answer the questions, What happened? and How did it happen? This might be modified somewhat, during an attorney's hypothetical question, to What *may* have happened? and How *may* it have happened? What attorneys seldom understand about reconstructionists is that they might not know what happened or may have happened or how, but they can often tell you in an instant WHAT *DIDN'T* HAPPEN. What reconstructionists cannot answer is WHY? This is the job of the jury.

"I think that reenactment showed that he had an intent to kill."

> \- District Attorney
> John Posey[2]

Frequently, attorneys try to bolster their cases for or against an alleged intent matter by disguising a question to an expert as something vaguely science-like in nature. Such a question might look like this: "Mr. Johnson, based on your expertise and your years of experience both with firearms and ammunition, and knowing the velocity in feet-per-second of the shot Mr. Defendant fired at his deceased wife in the hallway of their home, and knowing the distance from the casing found at the scene and the point where Mrs. Defendant fell dead, could you give us an opinion as to whether a shooter in the doorway at the east end of the hall could reasonably expect (read "*intend*") to miss his wife, firing it as he obviously did?" The answer, of course, is "No" or "Huh?", depending on how foolish you want the attorney to look.

Criminal prosecutors will call a firearm a "weapon," while defense attorneys will call it a "gun." When prosecutors talk about the defendant "aiming" and "firing" the weapon, defense attorneys respond with phrases like "where the barrel was pointing when the gun went off." The former will say "finger on the trigger," while the latter speak of "finger in the area of the trigger guard," and plaintiff attorneys suing gun manufacturers say "inadvertent physical movement in proximity to the negligently designed and defective trigger mechanism." All of these advocates have a vested interest in their choice of words (hence the term "mouthpiece"), which emerges in the wording of their courtroom questions to you. Just as you wouldn't allow attorneys to refer to a cartridge as a "bullet," you should not let them confuse an action with an intent or a gunshot wound with a bull's-eye.

Intent questions are often heavily draped in the sacramental robes of scientific jargon. At times they even sound reasonable in that they almost seem to appeal to one's common sense, as in: "Do you expect us to believe that the weapon discharged accidentally with Mr. Defendant *not* meaning to shoot his wife?" Well, yes and no. No one but the shooter, and often not even he, knows his true intent. And the reason we're all in court, of course, is so the jurors can try to determine the shooter's intent. But people who investigate shootings for a living are not in the intent business and should be particularly wary of those cleverly disguised questions, whether they come from an attorney "on your side" or an "opposing counsel."

"[The Expert] agreed under cross-examination last Wednesday that he was not testifying that either of the officers was aiming at Lawson's head when they fired six shots at the car after Lawson tried to run them down."
- The Toronto Star[3]

Of course, we've all faced the cross-examiner with the "Isn't it possible..." series of questions that's meant to end with a flustered witness wearily admitting that, "Yes, anything's possible." Attorneys slip intent questions into the dark corners of such Q&A marathons. Such as, "Isn't it possible that Mr. Defendant intended to fire a warning shot into his Siamese cat just to scare his wife?" The answer to this one is, "Yes, and it's possible that if his wife had been in Cleveland at the time, she wouldn't have gotten shot."

Most of the time an alert opposing attorney will leap to his feet when an improper intent question is posed. Sometimes, after a lunch hour, when the judge is napping and the jurors are nodding off, a lawyer will try to slide by a question of intent to the shooting reconstructionist on the witness stand. This is the time to ask for a repeat of the question or a clarification to highlight the words "intended" or "meant to" or "expected." If this doesn't work, it's time to proudly disavow any knowledge whatsoever of anybody's intentions, expectations, or what they meant to do or not do or might have not meant to do, etc. The easiest way to do this is to say, "I don't know what the shooter intended." If you don't, you can soon expect the other attorney to ask something like, "You don't know what was intended, *you* weren't there, were you?"

Q: So you can't—again, it's just your opinion as to where the bullet or where the defect or whatever it was in the—that was in—that actually was in the paint, you can't tell whether that would have hit anybody or was intended to hit anybody?
A: No, I can't determine any intent behind a bullet.

- Annette King[4]

Naturally you have formed private opinions about the intent of shooters in cases you've investigated, but you didn't (or shouldn't have been allowed to) stand up in court and declare these judgments aloud. Such opinions have no place in your testimony. Let the attorneys get into "what the shooter really meant to do" during their closing arguments. This is why judges frequently admonish jurors that "the arguments of the attorneys do *not* constitute evidence."

After all, we don't really know what the shooter meant to do, we couldn't. That's for a jury to answer: it's

- 126 -

called a verdict. If you look over at the accused shooter sitting with his lawyer, you probably wouldn't want to look inside his mind anyway, much less claim any scientific certainty about what *you* think that *he* intended.

Just because someone got shot and you did your job investigating it and you're here and the accused is there, it doesn't mean that you know what he *meant* to do. . .*no matter who asks the question.*

*   *   *

NOTES

1. Moenssens, A., Moses, R., and Inbau, F., **Scientific Evidence in Criminal Cases**, Foundation Press: NY, 1973, p. 17.

2. Posey, J., Marin County (California) District Attorney, "Scene of the Crime," **48 Hours: Hard Evidence**, CBS television, producer Rita Braver, May 13, 1992.

3. Crook, F., "Crown Ends Case at Officers' Trial," **The Toronto Star**, March 14, 1992, p. A-18.

4. King, A., Grand Rapids (Michigan) Police Department Crime Scene Technician, *61st District Court transcript*, MI v May, July 1992, p. 15.

Chapter Thirteen

Reconstruction and Reenactment

"This reconstruction appeared on the face of it to be not only
highly ingenious but practically flawless; and it was
conclusively proven to be completely wrong."

- Henry Rhodes
Crime and Clues

In a sense, all areas of criminalistics and investigation
are geared to the reconstruction of the criminal act. The
latent print examiner can "reconstruct" the position of a
suspect's hand on a door; the serologist can sometimes
"reconstruct" the stabbing victim's position from stain
patterns on clothing; the medical examiner can "reconstruct"
the wounding of a human body. A more precise look at
reconstruction, however, requires that we distinguish
between the terms reconstruction, re-creation, and
reenactment.

We can easily dispose of the term "re-creation," as it
is sometimes misused in reference to reconstruction. The
word re-creation means to form anew, especially in the
imagination, to recollect and reform in the mind. This might
be what advocates do in the courtroom with the spinning of

tales and flights of fancy, but re-creation is not the turf of the criminalist.[1]

The term "reconstruction" indicates the reassembling (as from remaining parts) of an item's original form, a putting together again. If a vase is broken into many small pieces, a craftsman would try to gather as many pieces as possible and attempt to fit them properly back together again. Some pieces might be missing; some fragments might fit together in more than one way. The final form of the repaired vase would, of course, depend heavily on the number of recovered fragments and the skill and experience of the assembler.

In crime reconstruction, the vase is a criminal event that has been shattered into numerous small pieces called "evidence." Given enough pieces, a reconstruction can determine which witness statements agree with the final shape of the reassembled facts and which are inconsistent with the result. As defined by the California Department of Justice, homicide reconstruction is "the process of utilizing information derived from physical evidence at the scene, from analyses of physical evidence, and from inferences drawn from such analyses to test various theories of the occurrence of prior events".[2]

As defined by accident investigators, reconstruction is "the effort to determine, from whatever information is available, how the accident happened. . .It involves studying the results of the accident, considering other circumstances, and applying scientific principles to form opinions relative to events of the accident which are otherwise unknown or are the matter of dispute".[3]

A simple description might define shooting reconstruction as **an examination of the circumstances and physical evidence at the scene of a shooting to establish how the incident occurred**. This covers both the accidental and the criminal shooting event. Note that all of these statements describe the scene (or "results") of the event. This is the difference between scene reconstruction and laboratory criminalistics; the former is generally performed in the field, whereas the latter is generally bench work.

The key, of course, is the application of scientific principles, which is (one hopes) common to both scene reconstruction and laboratory examination. The practitioner, as any good scientist, must be cautious and conservative, relying on the physical evidence when possible and verifying or rejecting the input of interested human parties, be they witnesses, participants, or lawyers. Reconstruction by its nature involves a process of elimination, where what is purported to have happened is measured against the story told by the items of evidence.[4] With insufficient information, the investigator may not be able to determine what actually occurred; however, even with a few clues, he may be able to say what did **NOT** occur. This is often the framework on which a reconstruction hangs—a series of answers that eliminate those events that did not happen.

This brings us to the subject of reenactment. The word "reenactment" means to act out or *perform* again. It has nothing whatsoever to do with scientific principles. The distinction between reconstruction and reenactment is a critical one. To confuse the two is to confuse crime scene analysis with a puppet show. Originally criminal reenactments by police investigators were performed in the presence of suspects in an effort to encourage confessions.[5] Today, a reenactment, whether it is two role-players in front of a jury box or an elaborate video simulation of digitalized human figures repeating programmed movements, is but a *demonstration* of a previously existing reconstruction.

Without a reconstruction, competent or not, there can be no reenactment. The exception, of course, is a reenactment of an event as it was seen by a participant or witness. This brings us back to the human element, the hearsay, upon which a reconstruction cannot solely rely. These sorts of reenactments are, at best, just re-creations of recollections, and have nothing to do with criminalistics or scientific principles. Reenactment producers are but skilled cartoonists, not analyzers of physical evidence. It is dangerous for the members of a jury to confuse the two terms.

The time element is important. The shooting reconstruction may be able to determine where the victim was seated and approximately where the shooter was standing at a given moment in time when the shot and the trajectory happened. The reenactment artist pretends to know the shooter's furtive steps approaching the scene, the movements of the victim's panicked head and face as he meets the shot, and the likely instant reactions of both participants during the shooting. This all-seeing, all-knowing attitude on the part of the reenactor is somewhat mysterious, because *no one* knows exactly what these things were like, often not even the participants. These things cannot be scientifically calculated or estimated, but the reenactor would have the jury believe that he knows, that this is how it looked and this is how it happened. The reenactment is less than bad science, it's non-science masquerading as science.

The shooting reconstruction completed by a knowledgeable investigator may take into account that Shooter X was standing in a certain area and that Victim Y was struck by a certain number of shotshell pellets from his waist to his upper back while running away at about the south edge of a parking lot; the investigator can then estimate with a fair amount of precision, given the pellet-count per load of the shotshell and the tested pattern of the shotgun, that the weapon was pointed (intentionally or not) within a couple feet to the left or right of the victim, *but only at that instant in time*. The events and actions leading up to and following the shooting are unknown to the investigator, except for the statements of possibly biased participants. This instant in time may be presented to the court as a diagram or model, but will only show the moment as ascertained by the trajectory reconstruction, not some imagined scenario.

The reconstruction of an automobile accident can give one a good idea about the motions of the vehicles just before and just after a collision, because these are based on speed calculations worked out from marks on the roadway, crush damage, post-impact travel, and a multitude of other items of true physical evidence. This sort of incident might become the subject of an animated reenactment, after a competent reconstruction, of course. A shooting incident, on the other hand, is seldom the valid subject of such display. No one, especially the investigator, knows for certain what the whole incident looked like from the shooter's point-of-view, the victim's point-of-view, or the viewpoint of any interested bystander. No qualified investigator would lay claim to such omniscience. The reenactor, however, seems to know it all.

The use of "virtual reality," or VR, computer simulations to reenact crimes in the courtroom has stirred up controversy in the legal community. This dissention is not so much due to the non-scientific basis of such video treatments, but mostly because the VR-programmed details so readily reflect the particular slant of the lawyer's side that produced the reenactment.[6] The VR marionettes can be made to move, dodge bullets, shoot (maliciously or accidentally, depending if it's a prosecutor's or defense attorney's program), fall down, die, or do whatever else the programmer desires. The facts, as revealed by an examination of physical evidence, are seldom as pliable and all-encompassing as the virtual treatment. True reconstruction seldom provides all the answers to all the questions.

This, finally, is the crux of the problem. Are jurors to believe that there is a real scientific basis for a computer-animated version of a shooting? Will they be instructed by the judge that the reenacted treatment is but one possible explanation for the incident? Or will the cautious jurist not allow the reenactor's video into evidence in the first place, based on its lack of scientific foundation, its editorializing of the known facts, and its propensity to fill in the blanks that cannot really be known?

* * *

NOTES

1. Chisum, W.J., "Crime Scene Reconstruction," California Department of Justice Firearm/Toolmark Training Syllabus, reprinted **Association of Firearm & Toolmark Examiners Journal**, Vol. 23, No. 2, April 1991, pp. 745-51.

2. Bell, W.P., "A Proposed Definition of Homicide Reconstruction," California DOJ Firearm/Toolmark Training Syllabus, reprinted **AFTE Journal**, Vol. 23, No. 2, April 1991, pp. 740-44.

3. Baker, J.S., **Traffic Accident Investigation Manual**, 2nd ed., Northwestern University Traffic Institute: Evanston, Illinois, 1975, p. 319.

4. Gross, H., **Criminal Investigation**, 4th ed., Ed. R. Howe, Sweet & Maxwell: London, 1950, p. 14.

5. Rhodes, H., **Clues and Crime**, Murray: London, 1936, p. 56.

6. Homilton, J., "Is VR Real Enough for the Courtroom?" **Business Week**, Oct. 5, 1992, pp. 96-105.

Chapter Fourteen

Demonstrative Evidence

Whether it is a chalkboard sketch, a miniature scene with armed toy figures, or a 3-D animated rendering on a video monitor, the courtroom representation of a shooting incident must be fair and accurate. The shooting incident, like the tire track or shoeprint case, lends itself readily to a visual presentation. The presenter, however, must restrict his display to that which he knows. The demonstration of a shooting reconstruction cannot be based on the mere recollection of participants or imagined scenarios conjured by the attorneys. It cannot purport to represent the movements of human beings where that movement (running, jumping, hiding, falling, etc.) cannot be ascertained or confirmed by the physical evidence. All such cartoon making is fraudulent and unscientific. Furthermore, it is easily manipulated to suit the side vouching its authenticity.

Clarity is the watchword here. The courtroom exhibit should be readable, in plain language, and free of unnecessary detail. Before one takes a diagram to court, one should display it at an appropriate distance (ten to twenty feet) to a small group of disinterested on-lookers (say half a dozen secretaries from the office). This sort of "dry run" test can save one a lot of time later in the courtroom. It does not work to show the display to lab people or crime scene personnel, who are used to viewing such diagrams and are familiar with the technical terminology of forensic science. It is also useful to lean a sketch against a wall, provide a short description of the scene and the evidence, and then pass out a short written quiz to the test viewers to see if they understood the salient points; this also gives the shy viewers a chance to anonymously ask questions that they might otherwise be afraid to express. This technique is especially helpful when the presentation includes some of the more complex illustrative elements, such as elevation and cut-away views or sections and intersections. With courtroom illustration, clarity saves time. And preparation saves headaches.

The vouchering attorney should be familiar with the shooting scene diagram and should understand what the presenter plans to show with it. It is unwise to thrust a diagram onto a lawyer in front of a jury and then wait for him to visually orient himself to which way is Up and which way is North and what those dotted red lines represent. Likewise, it can save everyone time and confusion if the opposing attorney is allowed to view the finished product and ask reasonable questions of the presenter *prior* to the in-court display. Other technical witnesses (police officers, medical examiners, etc.) should be allowed to review all diagrams to which they contributed informational input or to which they will be asked to reference in their testimony. Any eyewitnesses or non-technical civilian witnesses who are scheduled to testify in the case should be acquainted with the illustrations one plans to use. It is awkward to have a witness who does not recognize a diagram of his own residence or who mistakes a second floor sketch for a first floor. For non-English-speaking witnesses, it is helpful to include words *and* pictures; a diagram with a small picture of a casing, not just the words "EJECTED .25 AUTO CARTRIDGE CASE," can benefit both the witness and some unversed jury members.

Just as all shooting scenes are different, all courtroom displays of such scenes are different. Along with thorough photographic documentation, a clear courtroom diagram helps the jurors visualize the crime scene and understand the reconstruction. Whether one is working a chalkboard sketch or a computer 3D view, practice and preparation are essential.

* * *

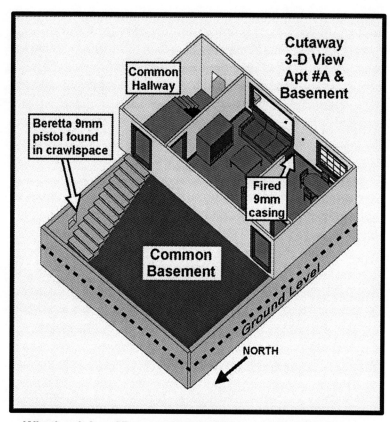

Cutaway 3-D View Apt #A & Basement

Common Hallway

Beretta 9mm pistol found in crawlspace

Fired 9mm casing

Common Basement

Ground Level

NORTH

Whether it is a 3D computer graphic or a chalkboard drawing, the key to a useful courtroom exhibit is clarity. Note that this illustration is an isometric projection, meaning that the near walls are the same size as the far walls. In a real-life view, the walls would shrink to a disappearing point. This is still a very useful exhibit.

Chapter Fifteen

Dealing with Medical Personnel

The shooting scene investigator must frequently deal with paramedics, ambulance crews, firefighters, hospital nurses and doctors, medical examiners, ME field investigators, and emergency room interns. For every one of the 39,720 patients who died from a gunshot wound in 1994, at least three others were injured seriously enough to be hospitalized. Gunshot wound injury occurs 90 times more often in the United States than in other industrialized countries, according to some recent studies. Every police officer has a favorite "World's Dumbest Emergency Room Screw-up" story, just as every ER nurse has a "Stupidest Cop" story. It works better just to get along, recognizing where your turf ends and where theirs begins. (I recall saying to a medical examiner that if I would forgive his office's fired drunk-on-the-job ME's assistant if he would forgive my department's retired notoriously-lazy-police-detective.) We have to work together.

The Notorious EMTs

An offhand remark by an Emergency Medical Technician at a crime scene can set things in motion, sometimes reeling out of control. An ambulance driver says, "The guy looks bad," and a minor gunshot wound case becomes a homicide investigator rollout. Another EMT remarks that the uncooperative victim's head wound is minor, and the cops clear the scene, only to find that the patient has died. Some paramedics are very good at diagnosing gunshot victims. This is to say that they can quickly evaluate entrance and exit wounds, probable internal organs struck, and the patient's chances of survival. Other EMTs are cop wannabees and attempt to estimate bullet caliber from wound size, determine trajectories, and involve themselves as much as possible with the scene investigation; this type of individual usually is a poor investigator and sometimes a poor EMT. Often the EMT lacks much information or is receiving mixed signals from the patient. The screaming and crying gunshot victim is frequently hardly wounded at all; the unconscious gunshot victim is only slightly wounded but almost dead drunk; the cheerful and talkative patient suddenly fades away and dies. It is good to understand the limits of the EMT's diagnostic abilities, but to keep track of which EMTs seem to have the knack for solid victim evaluation.

Learning to Get Along in the E.R.

It is imperative to have someone from the police inside the hospital emergency room with the shooting victim. This person should find an unoccupied wall space and stick to it. Just as you would not want doctors and nurses roaming around your crime scene, you do not want to get in their way *in their territory*. Early on, the emergency room personnel are in the same position as the EMT when it comes to the diagnosis of the gunshot patient. However, as clothing is cut away, the remainder of the body examined, and the vital signs taken, a much better picture of the patient's condition begins to emerge. In this early stage the assigned officer should not bother the hospital personnel with a lot of questions or requests for the victim's clothing; these can wait. As chest sounds are studied, X-rays taken, and wound depths determined, the pace of the emergency room either picks up in response to a failing victim or eases back in response to an improving patient. If the patient is rushed away to surgery, the assigned officer can find an emergency room nurse or physician to ask about the victim's condition, number and location of wounds, and can arrange for the collection of the victim's clothing. If the patient is improving and the pace has slowed somewhat, the officer can broach these subjects with someone who is not busy. The officer should try to approach someone who actually *worked on* the victim to receive the best, most immediate information. The X-rays can be very helpful if the officer cannot find someone to question. The size (large or small, not caliber), the shape (deformed, fragmented), and the number (two bullets of different size, fifteen shot pellets, 300 pellets) can often be seen on the X-ray films and make useful information for the crime scene workers. Besides the taking of a dying declaration from the patient, this initial information about the number, configuration (bullet path estimate, presence of exit wound, etc.), and prognosis is the most useful for the assigned officer to report back to the crime scene (as soon as possible). Even a brief report from the emergency room, such as, "Two wounds to the leg, no exits, non-life-threatening," or "One shot to the groin, deflected up into the chest, and he doesn't look good," or even "Stab wound only, no gunshot," can be extremely helpful to the on-scene investigators. The best information can be gotten by a conscientious officer who recognizes that he is but a bit player in the emergency room and that the goals of emergency room personnel go beyond evidence collection and other police concerns.

The Knife & Gun Club Doctors

With the advent of the emergency medical center concept, the field of emergency medicine has undergone vast improvements in the past twenty years. The so-called "knife and gun club" emergency rooms of metropolitan hospitals in America see gunshot victims nightly and are much better prepared to treat these patients than in years past. ER doctors are special breeds who seem to thrive on utter bedlam and those spur-of-the-moment, life-or-death decisions common to emergency medicine. Most are very good at what they do; those who falter or hesitate are quickly weeded out of the business. It is important for the police officer or evidence collector not to get in the way of these men and women. It is also good to remember that emergency room doctors are not forensic pathologists; their mandates are vastly different. Many questions about bullet tracks, exit vs. entrance issues, and ballistics problems are best left to the medicolegal expert. As helpful as many emergency room doctors try to be in this regard, such investigative problems are often beyond their means. Emergency interns and younger doctors often try to perform both the emergency medical function and the medicolegal function, usually with poor results.

Thousands upon thousands of shooting victims are saved by emergency room personnel in the United States every year and, for these cases, the crime scene investigator's only "wound ballistics" input is from the ER doctor. An experienced crime scene investigator working with a veteran knife-and-gun-club doctor can make a good combination. The investigator explains as much as he knows of the crime scene circumstances to the doctor, and the doctor shares what he knows about the bullet's interaction with the victim's anatomy. The doctor can use the crime scene data when he writes his medical notes, and the investigator can utilize information from the doctor in his crime scene notes. Given the right combination of cooperative personalities and an understanding of each other's professional territory, this can be a productive partnership.

Living With Your Medical Examiner

With almost 40,000 fatalities annually, gunshot wounds are second only to automobile accidents as the leading cause of injury death in the United States. According to the Federal Centers for Disease Control and Prevention, gunshot deaths will surpass traffic fatalities by the year 2003. Medical examiners and coroners are obviously busy people and getting busier. A trained, experienced, full-time medical examiner is the backbone of any criminal investigation involving death. If the ME is too overworked, too understaffed, or too politically inclined, the whole investigative process suffers. A medical examiner's office filled with motivated, knowledgeable, and professional people is a joy for both the police and the legal community. Conversely, an office beset with budgetary problems, internal power struggles, and battling egos is a curse to the criminal justice system. The medical examiner who needs to be begged and pleaded or wined and dined to do a thorough job or complete a report is not going to be of much help to an investigator, and there is seldom anything that an investigator can do about it. Shootings, however, do not occur in a vacuum; the bullets may lie in the body, and that body may be the jurisdiction of the medical examiner, but the ME's information from the body is only as good as the information from the scene in which that body was found. It is not a wholly separate process. The medical examiner, therefore, can use the crime scene information and can provide the investigator with a great deal of information in return.

There are certainly disagreements to be expected. The crime scene investigator who has not had some difference of opinion with a medical examiner is a rare beast. MEs, like crime scene investigators, doctors, nurses, cops, and lawyers, are not infallible. Medical examiners who are always in disagreement with crime scene investigators are often just self-centered and megalomaniacal, but MEs who never contradict an investigator's finding are also *not* providing any new information to the mix. It is a balance. Even if, on paper, the medical examiner's office is in charge of crime scenes involving death, the lines of authority break down to this: the ME has total authority for the body, because he or she is *responsible* for the body, and the crime scene investigator has total authority over the scene, because he or she has to *answer for the work done at the scene*. The crime scene investigator who listens to his medical examiner and the ME who listens to her crime scene investigator are in the best position to sort out the physical evidence. (And an attorney, prosecution or defense, who listens to both the medicolegal people *and* the crime scene people, has a profound advantage over an advocate who tries to steer the evidence to fit his case.)

In court, a crime scene investigator should not be asked to ponder questions about the nature and severity of wounds, the medical effects of the projectile on the body, or anything else having to do with the biology of "wound ballistics." The only body-type questions that can legitimately be put to a crime scene investigator are those in which the body is discussed simply as another *object* in the scene (i.e., intervening target, terminal point, pellet pattern interference, etc.). The attorney who tries to make a medical witness of a crime scene investigator is courting disaster. *Wound ballistics is the subject of medical testimony, not scene work testimony.* Testimony requiring a medical opinion also requires a medical education.

Listening to and learning from one's brothers and sisters in the medical profession can be a huge benefit to the crime scene investigator. It is critical to remember that their priorities are not your priorities, that sometimes these priorities come in conflict, that evidence will sometimes be lost or contaminated, and that they have their own battles to fight.

*   *   *

Suggested Reading

Goldberg, B., Von Borstel, E., Dennis, L., and E. Wall, "Firearm injury risk among primary care patients," **Journal of Family Practice** Vol. 41, No. 2, August 1995.

Headden, S., "Guns, Money and Medicine," **U.S. News and World Report**, July 1, 1996.

Whitecloud, T., Michas, P., Williams, R. and G. Dawson, "Gunshot wounds drain trauma center resources," **Orthopedics Today**, March 1996.

Chapter Sixteen

The Crime Scene Reconstruction Mind-Set

Crime scene reconstruction is generally misunderstood by the public, the media, the law enforcement community, the legal profession, and many crime scene people. Much of this confusion is based on differing understandings, definitions, and expectations of what reconstruction can and cannot do, and what reconstruction expert witnesses will and will not say. In some jurisdictions, the police detective is the source of the reconstruction; whatever he says happened is the basis for all further conjecture. In other jurisdictions, the prosecuting attorney conjures up a theory that can be propped up by whatever physical and eyewitness evidence he can assemble. In still other jurisdictions, no member of the police agency or crime lab is supposed to know anything about anything until the state's attorney goes out and hires a private reconstruction expert who can enlighten everyone and wrap all the evidence into a tidy little package for a jury. As it turns out, none of these characterizations is correct or very productive.

Rule #1:

Assume that the initial story is false

A general rule for all reconstruction and crime scene work is that one should approach the task as if everyone—all the cops, all the supervisors, and all the witnesses—are either lying about the facts of the crime, are incompetent, or are simply insane. That is to say, *all* the information is suspect. One should begin with as few preconceived notions and assumptions as possible. The "facts," as they are presented, should be checked and rechecked against the physical evidence. Information that is neither confirmed nor refuted by the physical evidence remains mere assumption; the crime scene reconstructionist should freely acknowledge this in court.

Rule #2:

There can be no reconstruction without physical evidence

While this seems basic enough, there are those who would conjecture at length about so-called "reconstructions" that are, in fact, wholly based on witnesses' memories and participants' viewpoints. This is *recollection, not* reconstruction. Furthermore, it violates Rule #1, that all such information should be assumed to be wrong.

Rule #3:

Attorneys do not do reconstruction

While it is true that reconstruction is a cooperative effort—with input from crime scene technicians, police investigators, medical examiners, and crime lab specialists—it is not true that attorneys (prosecuting or defending) are a part of the crime scene reconstruction process. Attorneys are advocates, pure and simple, and have no place in the search-for-truth that is crime scene reconstruction. When you find yourself going back to the crime scene time and time again to resuscitate the story line at the request of the prosecutor's office, you know that either A) you are not doing a thorough job of scene work, or B) the lawyers are running the crime scene investigation, or C) both. Often, a lead detective, serving as an advocate's assistant, will help a particularly manipulative prosecutor in steering the investigation. You have met people like this; we all have. They know they're right, and are offended by anyone who would question their spin on a sequence of events. They know they have their man and ignore other possible explanations for the role he might have played. And, of course, we all know defense attorneys whose goal is life seems to be entertaining us with the twisted scenarios that they have conjured. So, a very important rule of crime scene reconstruction is this: Attorneys are OUT (and this includes their lackeys and messengers).

Rule #4:
Politicians do not do reconstructions
Whether it is a police chief with a political agenda, a city mayor avoiding a public relations embarrassment, a crime lab director with higher aspirations, or a police lieutenant with a racist attitude, the political animals of our world have no place in the reconstruction process. Their input should be avoided and ignored. The crime scene workers should have a supervisor serving as a buffer between them and the politicians, protecting them from undue influence and pressure. The political process is not a scientific process.

Rule #5:
Cops-investigating-other-cops-in-the-same-agency do not do reconstruction
Imagine trying to investigate your own mother's murder when your brother is the main suspect and your father and sister are looking over your shoulder. The pressure would not be conducive to a thorough and scientific crime scene reconstruction. This is akin to the position we put crime scene people in when we ask them to investigate crimes within their own agencies. Whether or not the scene workers are unbiased and professional, putting them in such

a position is not fair. It also does not *appear* fair and objective.

Rule #6:

Reconstruction cannot answer all the questions

Short of an actual video recording of a shooting incident, as it is happening, a shooting reconstruction, like other scientific investigation, tends to leave you with certain gaps in your knowledge of the incident. Don't expect a reconstruction to answer each and every question. While reconstruction and the elimination of impossible scenarios may *point* to the truth of an incident, there will always be details that cannot be ascertained.

*   *   *

Appendix A:

Precision Without Accuracy in the Cruel World of Crime Scene Work

"Insanity is often the logic of an accurate mind overtaxed."

- Oliver Wendell Holmes

Recently I was examining a crime scene diagram on which the dimension "*99 feet 11.42 inches*" appeared for the size of a parking lot. Now, I immediately realized that this was a computer-generated sketch, but it occurred to me that the crime scene technician who had made the sketch *should* have a tough time selling it to a jury of mere human beings. The poor computer simply didn't know any better. The crime scene technician had fallen victim to the plague of Precision Without Accuracy, a malaise common to non-scientists, computer weenies, and used car salesmen.

The terms *accuracy* and *precision* are often used synonymously, to mean exactness or freedom from error. *Accuracy* is the degree of exactness actually possessed by an approximation or measurement. *Precision* is the degree of exactness with which a quantity is expressed.[1] It is possible to have precision without accuracy, as computers are wont to do. It is also possible to be accurate without being precise, which is actually the lesser of the two evils.

The aforementioned 99' 11.42" parking lot was of course the garbage-output of a computer that had not been reigned in to some significant figures. The fact that such a dimension appeared in the final version of the crime scene sketch meant that the technician had not realized that *expressing* exactness (precision) without *possessing* exactness (accuracy) produces impressively useless numbers. Such numbers are usually only practicable for engineers-talking-to-other-engineers and computers-interfacing-with-other-computers. While hundredths of an inch, microns, and nanometers are often of use in science and engineering, they are seldom of value on an exterior crime scene sketch. We are trying to make a fair and accurate representation of a crime scene, not build a new parking lot. The used car salesman quotes a price of "$16,999.95" to mean 17 grand; it may be precise, but it is neither accurate, nor particularly useful.

We should not surrender to the idea that 99' 11.42" is better than saying "approximately 100 feet," nor should we be the least bit impressed or overwhelmed by people who quote such numbers solely for the sake of exactness. Such a person, hounding the rest of us from his overly tidy office, is aptly described by the word "precisionist." Many people are awed by this type of individual and his "number crunching." Sometimes, juries are wrongly seduced by precisionistic witnesses. Instead, the jurors should be asking themselves: What kind of crime scene ruler distinguishes 42 one-hundredths of an inch from 43? And should we even care?

If the precisionist is so overly concerned with the 58/100ths of an inch missing from the 100-foot parking lot, maybe we should examine the rest of his work for an over-reliance on silly and inconsequential things.[2] Maybe his tape measure was cold and tight, or wet and loose, or worn and stretched; maybe the parking lot was really 101 feet. Maybe it was 99' 11.429" and he carelessly overlooked those extra nine one-thousandths. Maybe he weighs grams of cocaine on a truck scale. Maybe, in his efforts to wow the jury with his fastidiousness, he overlooked something un-fastidious like a bullet hole or bloodstain. Look at it this way; if he missed a whole foot in the 100-foot parking lot, he would only have a one percent error. But this guy has somehow figured out that 58/120,000ths of the parking lot are missing. Precision without accuracy should always be suspect, a red flag to the trier-of-fact.

The other problem here, besides the hoodwinking of juries, is that the precisionist's product constitutes a waste of court reporter's tape, report papers, work hours, telephone time, computer disk space, and general wear & tear on the brains of mere human beings who have to stop and mentally translate overly precise figures like 99' 11.42" into a meaningful number like 100 feet. This is not to say that hundredths don't have their place in the world; of course, they do. Where do you think gun calibers come from? Or nickels, dimes, and pennies? Or parts-per-billion tests for toxins? Precision has its place, obviously! Even on crime scene sketches, the very accurate measurement of a bullet hole height or angle is certainly appropriate. For parking lots, however, the nearest inch will usually suffice.[3] Workable decimals that are the product of good crime scene processing, not just the inadvertent discharge of a fraction-ejaculating computer, are certainly necessary. The key is to recognize the difference.

* * *

NOTES

1. **The International Dictionary of Applied Mathematics**, W.F. Freiberger, ed., Van Nostrand: Princeton, NJ, 1960.

2. Fox, R.H. and Cunningham, C.L., **Crime Scene Search and Physical Evidence Handbook**, U.S. Government Printing Office: Washington, D.C., 1973.

3. Baker, J.S., **Traffic Accident Investigation Manual**, Northwestern University: Evanston, IL, 1975.

Appendix B:

Why Crime Scene Reconstruction Does Not Answer the Why Question

"I tend not to try to determine why people do things in crime scenes."

- Criminalist Charles Morton
California v Menendez II
Trial transcript 12-5-95

Crime scene reconstruction may answer the question of *where* a victim was standing when an ax hit him or *who* stepped in the pool of blood by the door or *what* caused the revolver's hammer to fall or when the third shot hit the car window or *how* the knife ended up out on the patio, but the crime scene reconstructionist cannot answer the ultimate question, the final question that tugs at everyone's mind, the all-encompassing, all-seeing, all-knowing question of *WHY* did the crime happen? This may account for the fact that attorneys (for either side) very seldom ask "Why?" questions.

What happened and *How* it happened cover almost all of reconstruction work. The "Why?" question is an ultimate issue, something to be contemplated by ministers, psychologists, widows, and jurors. *How* a shot struck a victim is not the same as *Why* it struck the victim. Some very excellent works [*Bevel, Rynearson, Chisum*] on the subject of crime scene reconstruction mention *Why* as one of the questions answerable by the reconstructionist. These authors are more accurately addressing the questions *How*, rather than *Why*.

The true answers to the *Why* question of crime are often:

He always hated his mother

or

He just ran out of luck

or

She was as crazy as a couple of dancing mice that night

or

The guy owed him money, so he shot him

or

It was a lovers' quarrel

or

**Yes, he knew the gun was loaded,
but he didn't mean to shoot the store clerk**

or

The voice from the toaster told him to do it

or

**The police officer took his eyes off the suspect for just a
moment**

or

"I killed them to prevent any more earthquakes"

or

He hit her once too often

or

**The victim said something stupid like,
"You can't do it. Go ahead and shoot!"**

or

She hit him with his own car just to scare him

or

**His fifth grade teacher always thought he was strange
when
he talked about assassinating famous people
or
"Gee, I dunno. . .I guess I was pretty upset."**

These, after all, are the **real** answers to the "Why?" question. No amount of careful crime scene measurement, meticulous photography, painstaking evidence collection or Sherlock Holmesian deduction, induction, or reduction can answer the *"Why?"* question. No reconstruction has yet answered the Why of Jeffrey Dahmer, Ted Bundy, or John Wayne Gacy, but numerous individuals and agencies have addressed the "What happened?" and "How did it happen?" questions that surround these cases. (It was perhaps the downfall of those who have tried to reconstruct the Kennedy assassinations that they could never quite divorce the what-happened from the why-did-it-happen.) You *can* understand the How without knowing the Why. And this is not all bad, because usually the true reason *why* a crime occurred is neither very interesting nor very enlightening.

Sixty stab wounds and a shoeprint on the victim's face may *indicate* why the killer thought it was necessary to commit the act. The word "PIG" written on the wall in the victim's blood may *indicate* why the killer felt it was time for a murder. The use of meat fork *and* boning knife *and* roofing hammer or fifteen groin shots may *hint* at the true reasons why the crime was committed. These, however conspicuous, are only indicators of why. . .indicators to be interpreted by attorneys in their closing arguments, juries in their deliberations, and psychological profilers in their analyses.

As a crime scene reconstructionist, your job is not to answer *Why* the crime occurred. It's not your problem. You are employed to examine the evidence and circumstances and, with some knowledgeable and scientific analysis, figure out *How* the crime transpired. The "Why?" is not your specialty, nor your responsibility. There is an old cop maxim that says that there are two kinds of murder cases: who-done-its? and who-cares? In either type of case, the question of why who done it did it is *not* something that can be answered by a crime scene reconstruction.

NOTES

Bevel, T., "Crime Scene Reconstruction," **Journal of Forensic Identification**, Vol. 41, No. 4, 1991, pp. 248-54.

Osterberg, J. and Ward, R., **Criminal Investigation: a method for reconstructing the past**, Anderson: Cincinnati, 1992.

Rynearson, J.M. and Chisum, W.J., **Evidence and Crime Scene Reconstruction**, 3rd ed., National Crime Investigation & Training: P.O. Box 492005, Redding, CA 96049, 1993.

Appendix C:

Evidence Collection and Departmental Policy

After the examination, the photography, and the measurement of the crime scene, there comes the actual collection of the physical evidence. Various departmental policies and procedures, established practices, and some basic street practicalities come into play in the evidence collection process. What is right for the Criminalist in Los Angeles might not be right for the Evidence Technician in Washington, D.C. or the Scene of Crime Services Officer in London. These differences have as much to do with the day-to-day realities of crime volume and workload as they do with the specific policies of the servicing crime laboratories. In some jurisdictions, firearms are packaged and transported to the lab as they are found: no unloading, no fingerprinting, no nothing. In some agencies, swabbing the hands of suspects, victims, and suspected suicides for gunshot residue is standard practice; likewise, some crime labs accept gunshot residue samples so long as they were taken no more than four hours after a shooting, while other labs will not work on such specimens at all. Some laboratories conduct a full range of firearm function testing, test-firing for exemplars, and submission of test bullets to an "open case" file, while other labs perform only the tests specifically requested by the submitting agency.

Certain departments expect that the person collecting a firearm will document and remove blood and trace evidence from the weapon, fume it for fingerprints, and then package it for submission to a lab. Other agencies will have the laboratory examiner respond directly to the crime scene to collect the items himself. It is the practice of certain crime scene units to record measurements locating the position of each and every ejected cartridge case at a crime scene; others simply gather the casings in a bag and estimate the general location from which they all came. Certain departments block windows, darken rooms, spray luminol, and try to find bloodstains and trails; others use Super Glue fuming on whole houses; still other agencies "bag and tag" the victim's body, scoop up the casings and gun, and move on to the next murder on the "one homicide/one hour" schedule. Some collectors of evidence still get out a scribe and write their initials, case number, and other information on the nose or tail of each bullet they collect; others, who have been taught to disturb the evidence as little as possible, seal the item in an individual envelope and record the same information on the outside of the envelope. One agency may dictate that all victims' clothing is placed in paper bags; another may demand air-drying in a special cabinet or room; a third might have pizza-type cardboard boxes to keep items of clothing flat to preserve bloodstain pattern evidence and gunshot residue. Some departments are too busy. Some departments have uninformed people making policy. There are, however, right and wrong ways to do things.

In writing a departmental policy concerning the methods of collecting physical evidence, the person writing the policy (if it is written down at all) should first find out what the serving forensic laboratory demands and expects. If a lab won't perform examinations of gunshot residue kits, there is no reason to collect or submit such evidence. If a lab only accepts weapons that have not yet been unloaded and printed, there is no reason to do these things as part of collection practice. This is not to say that the policy must adhere to some kind of "wish list" of evidence collection dreamed up by lab people fresh out of a university forensic science program, who might be thrilled with the prospect of a crime scene investigator who vacuums the pavement around a shooting site for soil and trace evidence or expects every single glass particle from a shooting scene submitted in cotton-lined pill boxes. Neither should the policy be based on a deep-seated fear that *everything* is evidence (the Dempsey Dumpster Theory of evidence collection) or that every ignorant question by every defense attorney who once heard something about a "paraffin test" should be anticipated and accounted for in detail. An agency's evidence collection procedure should not be based on some old chart that the police chief remembered from a "police science" book he studied in a long time ago in the police academy. And, of course, it should not be based on the idea that "we've always done things this way." Doing things wrong for a long period of time doesn't make them right.

Once it has been determined what the local crime lab will and will not do, one should try to ascertain what the crime scene unit can and cannot do. Is there sufficient staffing to expect that two people can work a crime scene for the number of hours it may take to perform the expected level of collection? Are there enough personnel with enough training to not only conduct the field work and tests but to testify appropriately in court to the results of their work? Is the budget such that the agency can afford alternate light source equipment, but not the training to use it? Or is the budget one in which that the training and equipment are available, but the crime volume is such that the personnel are always needed elsewhere for other scenes? Do they have lasers or ultraviolet lights or luminol reagents or metal detectors or electrostatic print lifters or trace metal detection kits? Are they provided the tags and tape and packaging and chemicals and generators and fuming hoods and drying chambers and so on to do what's expected of them?

Are the crime scene people expected to work on all homicides or just the murders of "important" people? Are they limited to killings or do they work serious assaults and suicide scenes? Is the crime volume such that all they can do are the bare fundamentals, before they are called away? Do they work robberies and rapes, too? Do they work on "date rapes" and domestic violence cases? Do they perform crime scene work on burglaries, larcenies, and stolen automobiles or do they only work on cases where the loss exceeds a certain monetary limit? Do they work all the time on everything or just on the things that the shift captain thinks are important for his shift? Are the crime scene assignments doled out on urgency criteria or a first-come-first-served basis or on a catch-as-catch-can policy? In determining what one expects of a crime scene unit, one must first determine how calls for their service will be managed and by what criteria.

Are the crime scene people motivated? Do they have any morale at all? Are they civilian or sworn personnel? Are they civilian crime scene workers supervised by sworn personnel, uniformed sworn officers supervised by civilian lab director, or some other combination? Is assignment to the crime scene unit a punishment to officers who have somehow screwed up as street cops? Is it a "rubber gun squad" for officers who are too disabled or mentally unfit for other duty? Is the assignment considered a step toward some other lucrative and desirable position in the department? Is it a dead end or a holding pattern? Are there promotional opportunities or is it a career death trap? So, in determining what is collected and how it is collected, one needs to consider the following:

1.) What does the crime lab need?

2.) What do we expect of the crime scene people?

3.) Do we have enough crime scene people to do what we expect of them?

4.) Do we have enough equipment to accomplish what we expect of them?

5.) Do they have enough training to do what we expect of them?

6.) Do they have enough motivation to do what we expect of them?

Until these questions are answered, the small daily decisions about what to collect and how to collect it are simply matters of personal preference, individual initiative, and happenstance, which is no way to run a railroad or a crime scene unit.

* * *

Appendix D:

Protecting the Crime Scene

Ask crime scene technicians to name the biggest problem that they encounter on the job and you will consistently hear the same response--crime scene contamination by curious officers, detectives, and supervisors. Whether called evidence technicians, identification bureau officers, or laboratory specialists, either civilian or sworn, most personnel responsible for the processing of crime scene evidence find the same problems repeated by the same "offenders."[1] The unintentional contamination of crime scenes appears to be a problem that will not go away without written departmental policies reinforced by a strong foundation in training.

Very early in their careers, most law enforcement officers realize that the police work they see depicted on television and in the movies bears little resemblance to their jobs. It is something of an anomaly, therefore, that many of these same officers seem to believe that crime scene work should be performed as it is on the screen—murder scenes filled with loitering blue uniforms and multitudes of detectives hovering over bodies, with crime scene personnel appearing just long enough to snap an occasional picture or to dust a piece of furniture for fingerprints. Officers who work under this misconception do not seem to understand that a crime scene is not a cocktail party.

Widespread trampling of crime scenes can prove very damaging to investigations. Often, it results in several of the more sensitive forensic techniques—such as trace analysis, bloodstain interpretation, and DNA comparison—not being used to their fullest potential. Crime scene technicians know the futility of collecting hair or fiber samples after a roomful of officers has shed all over the scene. Footwear and tire track evidence is rarely recognized as valuable in departments where officers routinely wander unimpeded through crime scenes.[2] On occasion, this can seriously hamper investigations.

Not long ago, a sheriff's department was forced to conduct a mass fingerprinting of its detective unit after a particularly sensational homicide crime scene became overrun with curious personnel. Considerable time and effort went into eliminating officers' fingerprints from the pool of legitimate prints. In another case involving a different agency, a set of crime scene photographs showed supervisory personnel standing on a blood-soaked carpet.

When the integrity of fingerprints and shoeprints is jeopardized, it is time for agencies to rethink their approach to crime scene work. While departments have tried artificial means of scene protection—such as having visitors sign release forms agreeing to provide elimination fingerprints, hair samples, and semen specimens, or establishing two-perimeter crime scenes (the inner perimeter reserved for real forensic work)—these responses are mere salves for a problem that demands more meaningful attention.[3]

The role of detectives and supervisors in protecting crime scenes cannot be overstressed. These individuals ultimately are responsible for an investigation. Investigators who conscientiously limit the number of visitors to a crime scene ultimately may save themselves a great deal of legwork.

The simplest and most productive way for supervisors and detectives to discourage crime scene contamination is to set a good example by their own behavior. If a lieutenant walks around a crime scene at will, opening drawers and rifling through closets, what could be the harm in other officers doing the same? If a detective sergeant fails to implement a sign-in log for scene visitors, what is there to limit "drop in" visits by curious patrol officers? It is in the best interests of case investigators to set a good example and to make sure others follow it.

To further enhance the protection of evidence, police administrators should draft and enforce a written policy regarding crime scene protection and preservation. The policy not only must be clear but also must carry the same weight as any other departmental rule. Police administrators should not tolerate curiosity as an excuse for unchecked visits to the scene of a crime.

Administrators, perhaps in conjunction with the local prosecutor's office, should write and enforce the rules, and like supervisors and investigators, set an example by their own behavior.[4] Prosecutors who have lost cases due to crime scene contamination could be an invaluable source of ideas in the formation of policy. Likewise, administrators should take advantage of the technical knowledge of laboratory and crime scene specialists when formulating the department's policy.

The primary responsibilities of initial responders to a crime are to preserve life and to control suspects and witnesses. Then, shifting their focus somewhat, responding officers must take steps to preserve the integrity of the scene's physical boundaries. While this may not be a problem for those officers who were once taught the importance of protecting crime scenes, others—including supervisors, media relations personnel, and administrators—sometimes have trouble leaving well enough alone at a crime scene.[5]

A department's written policy should provide a uniform procedure to restrict unnecessary access to crime scenes. A crime scene policy should contain the following elements:

The officer assigned to the crime scene's main entry must log in all visitors, including name, rank, stated purpose, and arrival and departure times. Absolutely no undocumented visitors should be allowed in the crime scene area.

Every officer at the scene must complete a standard report describing their involvement and their specific actions while at the scene.

All visitors must make available any requested exemplar (hair, blood, shoeprints, fingerprints, etc.) for elimination purposes.

The highest-ranking officer entering a crime scene must assume responsibility for all subsequent visitors to the scene.

This final element means that any supervisory officer who visits the scene to "have a look around" must stay at the site until either the crime scene technicians finish their work or a higher-ranking officer arrives. Needless to say, this simple requirement goes a long way to discourage pointless tourism.

An officer attempting to secure a crime scene who finds the post regularly overrun by curious commanders must have the means to protect the scene, enforce department rules, and deal with superior officers. This is often a difficult balancing act. A clearly written, well-enforced policy helps to level the playing field.

In addition to a clearly defined written policy, departments should also address the problem of crime scene contamination by instructing new officers to follow approved practices. This is best accomplished during basic academy instruction by having crime scene specialists discuss the department's policy and the importance of protecting forensic evidence. As more officers become trained in proper practices, the risk of future crime scene contamination steadily diminishes. Crime scenes often yield forensic evidence that leads to the apprehension of dangerous criminals. Perhaps just as often, though, potentially valuable evidence is destroyed or rendered useless by careless behavior at the crime scene. Clearly written directives and training for new officers in this area will help agencies to resolve the problem. However, the ultimate responsibility rests with administrators, supervisors, and detectives to reinforce positive conduct by setting a good example for other officers to follow.

NOTES

1. R. Saferstein, Criminalistics: **An Introduction to Forensic Science**, 2d ed. (Englewood Cliffs, New Jersey: Prentice-Hall, 1981), 31-32.

2. W. Bodziak, **Footwear Impression Evidence** (New York: Elsevier, 1990), 16-17.

3. L. Eliopulos, **Death Investigator's Handbook: A Field Guide to Crime Scene Processing, Forensic Evaluations, and Investigative Techniques** (Boulder, Colorado: Paladin, 1993), 2.

4. V. Geberth, **Practical Homicide Investigation** (New York: Elsevier, 1983), 21.

5. J. Peterson, S. Mihajlovic, and M. Gilliland, *Forensic Evidence and the Police: The Effects of Scientific Evidence on Criminal Investigations*, **National Institute of Justice Research Report**, Washington, DC, U.S. Government Printing Office, 1984, 46.

A Model for Crime Scene Preservation Policy

I. <u>PURPOSE</u>: The purpose of this Procedure is to outline the proper methods of protecting the scene of a Major Case crime and thus create an environment wherein members of the Crime Scene Unit can more effectively recognize, record, and collect physical evidence. [*Definition: a Major Case crime is a crime-against-person involving death or life-threatening injury, including officer-involved shootings.*]

II. <u>BACKGROUND</u>: The scene of any crime is itself evidence. The observations and findings at an unchanged crime scene are vitally important to the successful clearance of a case. The improper protection of a scene will often result in the contamination or loss of physical evidence.

III. <u>GENERAL PROCEDURE</u>: Upon arrival at scenes of crime, Department personnel will render medical assistance; secure suspects, victims, and witnesses; <u>secure the crime scene</u>; and request by radio the appropriate supervisor, special units, and/or Major Case Unit.

A. Personnel will determine the perimeter of the scene and surround the area with yellow "Police Line" tape, vehicles, sawhorse barriers, or by other appropriate means. This perimeter will initially be established as wide as possible, as it is always possible to shrink the area later, but very difficult to enlarge a crime scene perimeter after a crowd of spectators has formed. For scenes involving roadways, the full length of the block may be barricaded against traffic movement; barrier tape must also be utilized at these scenes to limit sidewalk traffic.

B. Supervisors will direct the deployment of a sufficient number of patrol vehicles and uniformed personnel necessary to secure the area. No employee will release statements or other information to the public or media without approval from the Major Case Unit Supervisor at the scene.

C. ALL personnel will complete standard Incident Reports detailing their assignments and activities.

D. The natural egress or known point-of-entry to the scene will be protected. If possible, the scene supervisor will locate an alternative entry to the scene, and all subsequent foot traffic will enter and exit by this route until arrival of the Crime Scene Unit.

E. No deceased person will be moved, handled, or searched, except as directed by the Medical Examiner. Biohazard protocol will be followed.

F. Remote outdoor scenes will be processed by daylight whenever possible. The Major Case Unit Supervisor will arrange for overnight security and personnel for such assignments.

IV. CRIME SCENE SECURITY: Following the treatment and/or removal of any injured persons or the verification of death in a deceased person, the first responding officers will secure the scene against any and all entries by relatives, spectators, press, and other police officers. If at all possible, the scene officers will guard the scene from the exterior or from the immediate interior with a minimum of movement; the handling or moving of objects, weapons, etc. is prohibited in an already secured crime scene. *Any alterations or movement in the scene by any witnesses, emergency personnel, or police officers will be reported to the Major Case Unit investigators and must be included in the officer's Incident Report.*

A. The scene security officer will record all persons entering the scene, including name, rank, stated purpose, time-in, and time-out on the Sign-In Log. <u>There will be no exceptions.</u>
B. By registering on the Sign-In Log, each visitor agrees, if called upon, to provide any or all of the following samples for elimination purposes: blood, hair, handwriting, fingerprints, palm prints, footprints, fiber samples, footwear, weapons, and ammunition, etc.
C. The highest ranking Department supervisor who enters the crime scene will become responsible for maintaining all subsequent security for that scene.
D. The scene of a death investigation is the jurisdiction of the Medical Examiner, the Major Case Unit, and the Crime Scene Unit. *No other police personnel, command or otherwise, should be allowed to breach the boundaries of a secured crime scene.*

Appendix E:

Bad Science

Forensic science is the product of an uneasy and unholy mating of Science, the objective seeker of truth and knowledge, and Forensics, the argumentative persuader of courtroom advocacy. It is not called Justice Science, Law Science, or Truth Science, as many of us would like to imagine. We are a bastard child, an orphan, but still the subject of an intense child custody battle between our estranged parents, the truth seeker and the advocate. The tug-of-war goes on daily for our loyalties and confidences, each side offering candy and warm hugs. These separated parents have visitation rights. Sometimes they take our brothers and sisters away. Sometimes they don't come back.

We in forensic science like to think of ourselves as our mother's child—Mother Science, pure and incorruptible—and most of us start out this way. Some of us remain pure. Some grow up to be delinquents. The advocacy half of forensic science will not go away; it has weekday visitation rights and the power-of-subpoena. It has advocate friends called prosecutors, attorneys, cops, the press, and the Government. The advocates rarely understand the appeal of Mother Science, cannot fathom a search for truth in a game plan which calls for scores and trophies. They are constantly trying to persuade us to see it their way, to compromise, to bend just a little. They don't realize it, but what the advocates are asking for is Bad Science.

The pressure to be a Bad Scientist, to fit in and go along, is great, and it doesn't go away unless you put your foot down and say Enough Is Enough! And keep saying it to each supervisor, each detective, and each fair-haired boy from the prosecutor's office. Bad Science is what forensic science becomes when an attorney or prosecutor, who often display all the ethics of a full-grown hamster, get a forensic scientist to play ball, to get with their program and see their big picture. There is an old Bad Science joke about a scientist who was working with an ant. The scientist would cut off one of the ant's legs and shout, "Jump!" And the ant would jump. The scientist cut off a second leg, told the ant to jump, and again the ant jumped. And so it went, until the scientist had cut off all six of the ant's legs. This time, when told to jump, the ant did not jump. This proves it, the scientist concluded: when you chop all the legs off an ant, the ant goes deaf!

You may recognize some scenes from the following examples of Bad Science at Work. Some are laughable, others disturbing. Some simply haven't happened to you yet. I have not personally encountered all of these situations, but I know that each is true. If you haven't witnessed at least some of them, you will. If this helps you steel yourself against the onslaught of the Advocates, so be it. Finally, not all Advocates are malicious. Many, in fact, are simply not versed in the ways of good scientific method. When they ask for Bad Science, you can pity them as helpless people doing the wrong thing for the right reason. This type of Advocate needs to be taught. . .and watched.

Misinterpretation of Test Results

In a robbery case the victim, a bartender, testifies that the defendant had come into the tavern earlier in the night for a glass of beer. Three unwashed glasses were found at the scene and were processed for latent prints. Two of the glasses yielded prints, but these were of persons unknown, not the defendant. The prosecutor suggests that the print examiner testify that the third beer glass must have been used and then wiped clean by the defendant, because the other two glasses were obviously not his. The print examiner suggests that the prosecutor look elsewhere for this kind of testimony. The prosecutor looks surprised.

Manipulation of Raw Data

An accident reconstruction expert with a computer is hired by a plaintiff's attorney to determine the speed of the defendant's vehicle in a two-car collision. The expert enters into his computer program the road surface drag factor, skid and yaw mark lengths, and the location and severity values of the vehicle damage. The first run of his computer program produces an unrealistically high speed for the defendant's striking vehicle. The expert changes his drag factor estimate and tries again. The figures are still outrageous. Three program runs and several crush data changes later, the speed determination begins to look more believable. The defendant's attorney begins his attack with a subpoena for all five of the expert's computer printouts.

Jeopardy

As in the television game show where contestants reply in the form of a question, certain managers give their subordinates a desired answer and demand that they come up with the appropriate research questions to support it. During one police department's trial period of a 9mm pistol, a police officer wounds an assault suspect. Because the suspect was not instantly incapacitated, the police chief scraps the entire 9mm changeover program. He hears of the FBI's 10mm pistol program. One of the theories he returns with states that, by virtue of its "larger size," the 10mm is much better at striking blood vessels than the smaller 9mm bullet. The department's shooting instructor points out that en extra half-millimeter along on each side of the 10mm bullet's diameter would not really make much difference, unless you missed a blood vessel by half a millimeter with a 9mm bullet. Then the instructor begins his litany about the training budget, that training is at least as important as hardware, but the administrator doesn't hear him, because it's time to play Double Jeopardy with the police chief.

Comparing Apples and Orangutans

In a product liability suit, the plaintiff's attorney finds an expert witness who will testify that, if the shotgun involved in the shooting had as safe a firing mechanism as a rivet gun, the incident may not have happened at all.

Manipulation of Test Results

During a burglary trial, the prosecution produces seven latent prints recovered from inside the victim's house. The fingerprint examiner testifies that he has identified these prints as belonging to the defendant. The prosecutor suggests that the fingerprints are like seven little photographs of the burglar inside the house. Because he does not want a repeat of an earlier case lost to the defense attorney, the prosecutor calls a second examiner to the stand to verify the comparison performed by the first. The prosecutor then states that the seven latent prints, times two print examiners, make for fourteen little photographs of the defendant inside the crime scene. Later, when jokingly asked why he didn't call a third examiner to up the score to twenty-one fingerprints, the prosecutor replies that he had simply neglected to subpoena another print examiner.

Compulsive Computing

A .223 Remington bullet is found lodged in a house several hundred feet to the rear of a rifle practice range at which .223 weapons are frequently fired. The investigators want to know if it is possible for a .223 bullet to fly the several hundred feet necessary to reach the house, so they ask a firearms examiner. The examiner, who had recently invested in a ballistics program for his home computer, took down the range, wind speed, bullet shape, temperature, barometric pressure, and several other pieces of data. His computer charted the results. Finally, his answer to the investigators was, "Yes, it's possible." As a qualified firearms examiner, he had already known that the house was well within the range of the .223 cartridge and could have given the same answer when first asked the question . . . without computation.

Denial

In many major criminal investigations it is the practice of a detective unit to offer polygraph examinations to the suspects and, in cases of questionable accusations, to the victims. While they are not admissible in court, the polygraph results are relied upon as a valid investigative tool. One day a young police officer shoots and wounds a juvenile who he claims fired at him first, although no weapon is found. The officer claims he was also struck several times about the head and shoulders with a board prior to the shooting, although he exhibits no bruises, head injuries, or defense injuries to his hands or arms. When asked about this lack of consistent injuries, a detective reports that the young officer was wearing a bullet-resistant vest. The detectives do not offer the suspect or the officer a polygraph examination in this particular case.

Ethical Bankruptcy

In a homicide case the prosecution demonstrates a laser reconstruction of a bullet's path through a woman, which indicates that her husband fired a rifle from his shoulder height. The husband's story is that he was cleaning the weapon while it lay on a tabletop. The defense attorney finds a firearms expert who will claim that, while the weapon was not malfunctioning before the incident, was not malfunctioning when collected from the crime scene, and is not malfunctioning now at the time of trial, it may have suddenly malfunctioned and fired all by itself as a result of a buildup of dirt and powder within the weapon's mechanism on the day of the shooting. The expert does not address the issue of the shooting reconstruction, but the jury does and returns a guilty verdict.

No Scientific Methodology

A city truck driver runs a stop sign and causes an accident with serious injuries. Instead of relying on the skidmarks, crush damage, and scene evidence, the city authorities order a traffic investigator to conduct acceleration tests to determine the maximum possible speed the truck could have achieved in the one-block distance leading up to the crash. Because the truck involved was disabled in the accident, the traffic investigator uses a motorcycle to run the one-block acceleration test and reports back a peak speed of 35 miles-per-hour for the city truck.

Too Many Cooks Spoil The Broth

A city bus rear-ends and crushes a carload of teenagers, killing four. The first traffic investigators at the scene measure the skidmarks of the bus and determine that the bus driver was speeding. A national civil rights leader says the bus driver is being made a scapegoat by the city solely because he is a racial minority. The follow-up investigation by city authorities reports that the original traffic investigators, who have been abruptly removed from the case, must have been measuring tire marks tracked through melted roadway tar and that, on second thought, the city bus driver was not really speeding. A local television station gets a radar gun and reports that most drivers, including all city bus drivers, regularly exceed the speed limit on this section of road. Tire tracks in tar look nothing like skidmarks to the trained eye of the traffic investigator. Excessive speed aside, it is unlawful to follow another vehicle at an unsafe distance in that state.

Pursuit of the Inconsequential

In the faked robbery of a fast food restaurant, the night manager shoots to death an employee in a walk-in cooler, hides the "stolen" money and a .357 Magnum revolver, and calls the police. The crime scene personnel notice fallen dust on a restroom floor and discover the money hidden in a ceiling panel. The revolver is found among the night manager's possessions. In preparation for trial, the prosecutor asks for a shooting sound test to be done inside the restaurant's cooler. This, he says, will determine whether or not the fatal shots could have been heard by a teenage girl who was having sex with a man (not her boyfriend) in her boyfriend's van parked across the street from the restaurant. The girl, who incidentally had a full-length cast on her leg at the time (another mystery altogether), did not recall hearing much of anything, least of all gunfire. Her partner that night also somehow missed the sounds. The crime scene investigator refused to participate in such an experiment, arguing that it was invalid, irrelevant, and silly. . .and what would it prove anyway? The prosecutor suggested that the defense might use the fact that the girl had not heard the shots to argue that the time of the murder was somehow different. "Then let the defense make a sound test," the investigator says, leaving. The prosecutor is insistent. After being turned down by the police firearms trainer and the state regional laboratory examiners, the prosecutor gets three detectives to fire the shots for the sound test. To duplicate the sounds of a .357 Magnum, they load the weapon with light .38 Special target loads; they fire the quieter ammunition into a sandbagged pipe inside the walk-in cooler so as not to make holes in the walls. It is several months later, and the air temperature is sixty degrees lower than the night of the murder. By the time the test begins, the noisy morning rush hour traffic has clogged the street in front of the restaurant. To duplicate the hearing of the busy girl with the cast on her leg and other things on her mind, they use the prosecutor's ears as he stands across the street. (Later there were several profane allegations about what the prosecutor had to endure to fully recreate the event.) The results of the test? "It sounded like a hand clap," said one of the detectives stationed in the restaurant's dining room. So, apparently, one can induce deafness by making love to a girl in a full-length leg cast, the same as one can by cutting all six legs off an ant.

Examples of truly Bad Science are everywhere. So, what can one do to avoid ambush by the Bad Scientists? Three small philosophical exercises come to mind. The first is a methodological battle plan called "Ockham's Razor," named after the 14th century philosopher William of Ockham. In philosophy, it says that a problem should be stated in its basic and simplest terms. In science, according to Ockham's Razor, the theory that fits the facts of a problem with the fewest number of assumptions is the one that should be selected. This is the great-grandfather of the K.I.S.S. (Keep It Simple, Stupid) theory, and it works well against Bad Scientists.

The second tactic is termed "reductio ad absurdum," which is the disproof of a proposition (or stupid experiment) by showing the absurdity to which it leads when carried out to its logical conclusion. A good example of such a situation is the aforementioned case of the prosecutor who argued that seven fingerprints identified by two print examiners make a total of fourteen little traces of the burglar defendant. The reduction ad absurdum of that case is the notion that a third print examiner would up the ante to twenty-one clues, or that a dozen examiners identifying a single fingerprint would make for 12 traces of the suspect. The clues multiply like bunny rabbits. The mind boggles. Think of where the Bad Scientist is trying to lead you and look to the dark at the end of the tunnel.

The final fallback is to common sense, the bane of Bad Scientists the world over. It was Thomas Huxley who said, "Science is simply common sense at its best—that is, rigidly accurate in observation and merciless to fallacy in logic." This is where juries trod on the best-laid plans of eloquent attorneys. They step back for a moment and resort to instinct, to common sense. Lawyers, especially those True Believers who do the prosecuting, are notoriously bad at feigning common sense. They are better at reduction ad absurdum. Cops, on the other hand, are excellent at instinct and common sense, but poor on seeing the absurdity of a proposition's logical conclusion.

Lastly, one needs to stand one's ground. And this means more than just Do Not Testify To Methods Beyond Your Expertise or Do Not Selectively Ignore Evidence To The Contrary or Do Not Overstate Your Qualifications. Standing your ground means you have to get in the face of anyone who even hints at being a Bad Scientist. You'll need to gently redirect the novice Bad Scientist at times, showing him the light and letting him know where you stand. With the more seasoned advocates (prosecution OR defense), you may need a chainsaw to carve out your turf in the Bad Scientist's office, be it a medical examiner's office, a lawyer's office, or a supervisor's office. Draw the line. Let them know that Enough Is Enough. After all, you're the bastard child of both Science and Forensics. They'll expect you to be incorrigible. J. Robert Oppenheimer said it best when he wrote: "The scientist is free, and must be free to ask any question, to doubt any assertion, to seek any evidence, to correct any errors."

*   *   *

Sources for Shooting Investigation Equipment & Supplies

Chief Architect (3D graphics software)
Advanced Relational Technology Inc.
301 North Third Street
Coeur d'Alene, ID 83814
1-800-482-4433
1-208-666-0518

CorelDRAW! (graphics software)
North America
Corel Corporation
1600 Carling Avenue
Ottawa, Ontario
Canada
K1Z 8R7
1-800-772-6735

EVI-PAQ (crime scene supplies)
P.O. Box 18276
Tucson, AZ 85731
1-800-377-0450
1-520-751-1704

Kinderprint Company, Inc. (crime scene supplies)
P.O. Box 16
Martinez, Ca. 94553
1-800-227-6020

Lightning Powder Company (crime scene supplies)
1230 Hoyt Street, S.E.
Salem, Oregon 97302-2121
1-800-852-0300

Lynn Peavey Company (crime scene supplies)
P.O. Box 14100
Lenexa, Kansas 66285-4100
1-800-255-6499

Sirchie (crime scene supplies)
100 Hunter Place
Youngsville NC 27596
1-919-554-2244
1-800-356-7311

Bibliography

Bell, W.P., "A Proposed Definition of Homicide Reconstruction," California Department of Justice Firearm/Toolmark Training Syllabus, reprinted **AFTE Journal**, Vol. 23, No. 2, April 1991, pp. 740-744.

Bergman, P. and Springer, E., "Bullet Hole Identification Kit: Case Report," **Journal of Forensic Sciences**, Vol. 32, No. 3, May 1987, pp. 802-805.

Bevel, T., "Crime Scene Reconstruction," **Journal of Forensic Identification**, Vol. 41, No. 4, 1991, pp. 248-254.

Birkoff, G. "Ricochet off Land Surfaces," **Ballistic Research Laboratory Report 535**, Aberdeen Proving Ground, MD, Mar. 21, 1945.

Boehm, A.P., "Bullet Holes/Shotgun Patterns in Metal Screens," **Association of Firearm and Tool Mark Examiners Journal**, Vol. 9, No. 2, July 1977, pp. 181-187.

Breitenecker, R. and Senior, W., "Shotgun Patterns; an experimental study on the influence of intermediate targets," **Journal of Forensic Science**, Vol. 12, No. 2, 1967, pp. 193-204.

Burke, T.W. and Rowe, W.F., "Bullet Ricochet: A Comprehensive Review," **Journal of Forensic Sciences**, Vol. 37, No. 5, Sept. 1992, pp. 1254-1260.

Carr, J.C., "An Alternative Device for Distance Measurement in Range Determination Tests," **AFTE Journal**, Vol. 24, No. 1, Jan. 1992, pp. 76-78.

Carter, R.D., "A Case Solved Through Teamwork," **AFTE Journal**, Vol. 15, No. 2, April 1983, pp. 62-63.

Cashman, P.J., "Projectile Entry Angle Determination," **Journal of Forensic Sciences**, JFSCA, Vol. 31, No. 1, Jan. 1986, pp. 86-91.

Chisum, W.J., "Crime Scene Reconstruction," California Department of Justice Firearm/Toolmark Training Syllabus, reprinted **AFTE Journal**, Vol. 23, No. 2, April 1991, pp. 745-751.

Cook, C.W., "Ballistics and the Firearms Examiner," **AFTE Journal**, Vol. 10, No. 2, June 1978, pp. 49-51.

Cook, C.W., "Bullet Hole Size Information," **AFTE Journal**, Vol. 15, No. 4, Oct. 1983, pp. 53-55.

Courtney, M. and Hueske, E., "The Use of Hand-held Laser Pointers in the Reconstruction of Events at Crime Scenes," **AFTE Journal**, Vol. 26, No. 3, July 1994, pp. 170-172.

Fackler, M.L., Woychesin, S.D., Malinowski, J.A., Dougherty, P.J. and Loveday, T.L., "Determination of Shooting Distance from Deformation of the Recovered Bullet," **Journal of Forensic Sciences**, JFSCA, Vol. 32, No. 4, July 1987, pp. 1131-1135.

Fricke, C.W. and Payton, G.T., **Criminal Investigation and the Law**, 7th ed., Legal Books: Los Angeles, 1974.

Federal Bureau of Investigation, "Bouncing Bullets," **FBI Law Enforcement Bulletin**, Vol. 38, Oct. 1969, pp. 1-9.

Finstad, S., **Ulterior Motives, the killing and dark legacy of tycoon Henry Kyle**, William Morrow: NY, 1987.

Fisher, B.A., **Techniques of Crime Scene Investigation**, 5th ed., CRC Press: Boca Raton, FL, 1993.

Fletcher, G.P., **A Crime of Self-Defense**, Macmillan: NY, 1988.

Garrison, D.H.,"The Effective Use of Bullet Hole Probes in Crime Scene Reconstruction," **AFTE Journal**, Vol. 28, No. 1, Jan. 1996, pp. 57-63.

Garrison, D.H., "Examining Auto Body Penetration in the Reconstruction of Vehicle Shootings," **AFTE Journal**, Vol. 27, No. 3, July 1995, pp. 209-212.

Garrison, D.H., "Field Recording and Reconstruction of Angled Shot Pellet Patterns," **AFTE Journal**, Vol. 27, No. 3, July 1995, pp. 204-208.

Garrison, D.H., "Intent Behind the Bullet," **AFTE Journal**, Vol. 25, No. 4, Oct. 1993, pp. 294-296.

Garrison, D.H., "Little Gunmen: Shooting Reconstruction Miniatures," **AFTE Journal**, Vol. 23, No. 3, July 1991, pp. 836-848.

Garrison, D.H., "Reconstructing Bullet Paths with Unfixed Intermediate Targets," **AFTE Journal**, Vol. 27, No. 1, Jan. 1995, pp. 45-48.

Garrison, D.H., "Reconstructing Drive-by Shootings from Ejected Cartridge Case Location," **AFTE Journal**, Vol. 25, No. 1, Jan. 1993, pp. 15-20.

Garrison, D.H., "Shooting Reconstruction vs Shooting Reenactment," **AFTE Journal**, Vol. 25, No. 2, April 1993, pp. 125-127.

Geberth, V., **Practical Homicide Investigation**, Elsevier: NY, 1983.

Gieszl, R., "Stabilization of Glass Fractures," **AFTE Journal**, Vol. 22, No. 4, Oct. 1990, p. 440.

Gold, R.E. and Schecter, B., "Ricochet Dynamics for the Nine-Millimetre Parabellum Bullet," **Journal of Forensic Sciences**, Vol. 37, No. 1, Jan. 1992, pp. 90-98.

Government Printing Office, **Report of the President's Commission on the Assassination of President John F. Kennedy**, Washington, D.C., 1964.

Haag, L.C., "Bullet Impact Spalls in Frangible Surfaces," **AFTE Journal**, Vol. 12, No. 4, Oct. 1980, pp. 71-74.

Haag, L.C., "Bullet Ricochet: An Imperical [sic] Study and a Device for Measuring Ricochet Angle," **AFTE Journal**, Vol. 7, No. 3, Dec. 1975, pp. 44-51.

Haag, L.C., "Bullet Ricochet from Water," **AFTE Journal**, Vol. 11, No. 3, July 1979, pp. 27-34.

Haag, L.C., "The Construction of an Inexpensive Portable Laser for Use in Shooting Reconstructions," **AFTE Journal**, Vol. 19, No. 2, April 1987, pp. 175-177.

Haag, L.C., "The Forensic Use of Exterior Ballistic Calculation," **AFTE Journal**, Vol. 11, No. 1, Jan. 1979, pp. 13-19.

Haag, L.C., "An Inexpensive Method to Assess Bullet Stability in Flight," **AFTE Journal**, Vol. 23, No. 3, July 1991, pp. 831-835.

Haag, L.C., "The Measurement of Bullet Deflection by Intervening Objects and the Study of Bullet Behavior After Impact," **AFTE Journal**, Vol. 19, No. 4, Oct. 1987, pp. 382-387.

Haag, L.C., "A New Tool in Studying Selected Exterior and Terminal Ballistic Events of Forensic Interest," **AFTE Journal**, Vol. 28, No. 1, Jan. 1996, pp. 32-40.

Haag, L.C. and Kokanovich, J., "A Shot in the Dark: A Procedure for the Photographic Documentation of Firearms' Muzzle Flash," **AFTE Journal**, Vol. 23, No. 4, Oct. 1991, pp. 910-918.

Hartline, P., Abraham, G. and Rowe, W.F., "A Study of Shotgun Ricochet from Steel Surfaces," **Journal of Forensic Sciences**, Vol. 27, No. 3, July 1982, pp. 506-512.

Hueske, E.E., "Calculation of Trajectory Angles Using an Inexpensive Angle Gauge," **AFTE Journal**, Vol. 25, No. 3, July 1993, pp. 231-233.

Jauhari, M., "Approximate Relationship Between the Angles of Incident and Ricochet for Practical Application in the Field of Forensic Science," **Journal of Criminal Law, Criminology and Police Science**, Vol. 62, 1970, pp. 122-125.

Jordan, G.E., Bratton, D.D., Donahue, H.C.H. and Rowe, W.F., "Bullet Ricochet from Gypsum Wallboard," **Journal of Forensic Sciences**, JFSCA, Vol. 33, No. 6, Nov. 1988, pp. 1477-1482.

Lattig, K.N., "The Determination of the Angle of Intersection of a Shot Pellet Charge with a Flat Surface," **AFTE Journal**, Vol. 14, No. 3, July 1982, pp. 13-17.

Lee, H.C., **Crime Scene Investigation**, Central Police University Press: Taiwan, 1994.

Lindman, D.A. and Papke, R.E., "Range Determination by a Different Method," **AFTE Journal**, Vol. 23, No. 3, July 1991, pp. 856-857.

MacDonell, H.L., "Ballistics—a case example of deductive reasoning from unusual physical facts," **Law Enforcement Science and Technology II**, Vol. 2, (S.I. Cohn, editor), IIT Research Institute, 1968, pp. 365-371.

MacDonell, H.L. and Lewis, A.A., **The Evidence Never Lies**, Holt, Rinehart: NY, 1984.

Maxey, R.R., "Fracture Analysis of Tempered Glass," **AFTE Journal**, Vol. 15, No. 2, April 1983, pp. 114-116.

McConnell, M.P., Triplett, G.M. and Rowe, W.F., "A Study of Shotgun Pellet Ricochet," **Journal of Forensic Sciences**, Vol. 26, No. 4, Oct. 1981, pp. 699-709.

McCumber, D., **X-Rated: the Mitchell brothers: a true story of sex, money, and death**, Simon & Schuster: NY, 1992.

Mitosinka, G., "Technique for Determining and Illustrating the Trajectory of Bullets," **Journal of the Forensic Science Society**, Vol. 11, 1971, pp. 55-61.

Molnar, S. Jr., "Use of Scale Drawings to Establish Facts in Shooting Cases," **AFTE Newsletter**, No. 6, Feb. 1970, p. 25.

Molnar, S. Jr., "What is a Firearms Examiner: Some Provocative Thoughts," **AFTE Newsletter**, No. 8, June 1970, p. 36.

Nennstiel, R., "Accuracy in Determining Long-Range Firing Position of Gunmen," **AFTE Journal**, Vol. 17, No. 1, Jan. 1985, pp. 47-54.

Nennstiel, R., "Determination of the Line of Sight Angle through Firing Experiments," **AFTE Journal**, Vol. 23, No. 4, Oct. 1991, pp. 919-924.

Nennstiel, R., "Forensic Aspects of Bullet Penetration of Thin Metal Sheets," **AFTE Journal**, Vol. 18, No. 2, April 1986, pp. 18-48.

Nennstiel, R., "Study of Bullet Ricochet on a Water Surface," **AFTE Journal**, Vol. 16, No. 3, July 1984, pp. 88-93.

Nicolosi, F.M., "Ballistics Alignment Laser," **AFTE Journal**, Vol. 24, No. 1, Jan. 1992, pp. 65-68.

O'Brien, M.W., "Scale Model Use in Criminal Trials," **Journal of Forensic Identification**, Vol. 39, No. 6, 1989, pp. 359-366.

Omilion, P.M., "The Effects of Window Glass on Shotgun Pellets Patterns," **AFTE Journal**, Vol. 11, No. 4, Oct. 1979, pp. 54-57.

Osterburg, J. and Ward, R., **Criminal Investigation, a method for reconstructing the past**, Anderson: Cincinnati, 1992.

Patty, J., McJunkins, S. and Murdock, J., "Associating Recovered Bullets with Ricochet Sites," **AFTE Journal**, Vol. 7, No. 2, July 1975, pp. 28-32.

Petraco, N. and DeForest, P.R., "Trajectory Reconstructions I: Trace Evidence in Flight," **Journal of Forensic Sciences**, Vol. 35, No. 6, Nov. 1990, pp. 1284-1296.

Prendergast, J.M., "Determination of Bullet Impact Position from the Examination of Fractured Automobile Glass," **AFTE Journal**, Vol. 26, No. 2, April 1994, pp. 107-118.

Rathman, G.A., "Bullet Impact Damage and Trajectory Through Auto Glass, **AFTE Journal**, Vol. 25, No. 2, April 1993, pp. 79-86.

Rathman, G.A., "Bullet Ricochet and Associated Phenomena," **AFTE Journal**, Vol. 19, No. 4, Oct. 1987, pp. 374-381.

Rathman, G.A., "The Effects of Material Hardness on the Appearance of Bullet Impact Damage," **AFTE Journal**, Vol. 20, No. 3, July 1988, pp. 300-305.

Roberts, J. and Hamby, J., "Reconstruction of a Shooting to Prove/Disprove Trajectory," **AFTE Journal**, Vol. 17, No. 2, April 1985, pp. 53-55.

Rynearson, J.M. and Chisum, W.J., **Evidence and Crime Scene Reconstruction**, 3rd ed., National Crime Investigation & Training: Redding, CA, 1993.

Sharma, B.R., **Firearms in Criminal Investigation and Trials**, N.M. Tripathi Private Limited: Bombay, 1976.

Silliman, J.R., "Crime Scene Search: Evidence at the Scene of a Shotgun Shooting," **AFTE Journal**, Vol. 9, No. 2, July 1977, pp. 111-118.

Smith, L.L., "Bullet Holes in Glass," reprinted **AFTE Newsletter**, No. 10, Oct. 1970, pp. 14-15.

Stone, R.S., "Calculation of Trajectory Angles Using a Line Level," **AFTE Journal**, Vol. 25, No. 1, Jan. 1993, pp. 21-24.

Stowers, C., **Innocence Lost**, Pocket Books: New York, 1990.

Thornton, J.I. and Cashman, P.J., "The Effect of Tempered Glass on Bullet Trajectory," **Journal of Forensic Sciences**, JFSCA, Vol. 31, No. 2, April 1986, pp. 743-746.

Thornton, J.I. and Cashman, P.J., "Glass Fracture Mechanism—A Rethinking," **Journal of Forensic Sciences**, JFSCA, Vol. 31, No. 3, July 1986, pp. 818-824.

Thornton, J. and Guarino, K., "Polyethylene Shotshell Buffer and the Determination of Trajectory," **AFTE Journal**, Vol. 16, No. 3, July 1984, pp. 132-133.

Trahin, T.L., "Bullet Trajectory Analysis," **AFTE Journal**, Vol. 19, No. 2, April 1987, pp. 124-150.

Trilling, D., **Mrs. Harris: the death of the Scarsdale diet doctor**, Harcourt: New York, 1981.

Van Arsdale, M., "Determining Bullet Trajectory From a Ricochet off Windshield Glass," **AFTE Journal**, Vol. 30, No. 2, Spring 1998, pp. 309-315.

Wallace, J.S., "Bullet Strike Flash," **AFTE Journal**, Vol. 20, No. 3, July 1988, pp. 294-295.

Warren, G., "Simple Measurement of Angles of Elevation," **AFTE Journal**, Vol. 23, No. 3, July 1991, p. 869.

Zeldes, I., "Laser Beam: a New Tool for the Firearms Examiner," **AFTE Journal**, Vol. 13, No. 4, Oct. 1981.
p. 21-24.

CPSIA information can be obtained at www.ICGtesting.com
Printed in the USA
BVOW071138250712

296128BV00001B/174/A